UK Price
£4.95

2-50

AN ILLUSTRATED GUIDE TO
BATTLESHIPS
AND BATTLECRUISERS

Published by Salamander Books Limited
LONDON

AN ILLUSTRATED GUIDE TO
BATTLESHIPS
AND BATTLECRUISERS

John Jordan

A Salamander Book

© 1985 by Salamander Books Ltd.,
Salamander House,
27 Old Gloucester Street,
London WC1N 3AF,
United Kingdom

ISBN 0 86101 200 3

All correspondence concerning the
contents of this volume should be
addressed to Salamander Books Ltd.

Distributed in the United Kingdom
by Hodder & Stoughton Services,
PO Box 6,
Mill Road,
Dunton Green,
Sevenoaks,
Kent TN13 2XX

Photographs: The publishers wish
to thank the many official archives
and private collections which have
supplied photographs for this book.
We particularly thank Tony Gibbons
and Ray Burt for the use of their
pictures.

Credits

Author: John Jordan is a
contributor to many important
defence journals, a consultant for
the Soviet section of *Jane's
Fighting Ships 1980–81*, co-author
of Salamander's *Balance of Military
Power,* and author of three
companion "Guides": *The Modern
US Navy, The Modern Soviet Navy,*
and *Modern Naval Aviation.*

Managing Editor: Philip de Ste. Croix
Project Manager: Roger Chesneau

Colour artwork: © Tony Gibbons
of Linden Artists Ltd., 1983
Line artwork: Alan Hollingbery
and John Roberts
© Salamander Books Ltd.
Filmset: The Old Mill, London

Printed: Henri Proost et Cie, Belgium

Contents

Introduction

Before 1921, the limitations on capital ship construction were purely of a technical nature, and as technology advanced so battleships grew in size and in firepower. Major gun calibres grew from 11in (280mm) and 12in (305mm) to 14in (356mm) and 15in (381mm), and finally to 16in (406mm) and 18in (457mm) for the battleships completed or projected during the immediate postwar period, whilst new, heavily armed battlecruisers planned by the major powers approached 50,000 tons in displacement. In the difficult financial climate which followed World War I it seemed imperative to halt these developments, in order to prevent a new arms race involving the established naval superpowers, Britain and the United States, and the young but ambitious Imperial Japanese Navy. The result was the Washington Conference of 1921.

The ships projected at the time of the Conference would have outclassed even the battleships under construction in 1919–20, and it was therefore necessary to restrict battleship size and gun calibre in such a way that the Marylands of the US Navy and the Japanese *Nagato* and *Mutsu* would represent the ultimate in capital ship development for many years to come. Upper limits of 35,000 tons standard displacement and 16in (406mm) gun calibre were therefore incorporated in the terms of the Treaty that resulted from the Conference. At the same time, a "battleship holiday" was decreed —

Below: The British *Dreadnought* was the world's most powerful battleship at the time of her completion in 1906. By 1920, however, vessels of more than twice her displacement were being projected, armed with guns of 16in or even 18in calibre.

Above: Throughout the 1920s and 1930s, the basic fleet formation continued to be the battle line. This photograph shows a squadron of British "R" class battleships on manoeuvres during the early 1920s. The ship in the foreground is *Royal Oak*.

no new battleships would be laid down for ten years — and the relative strengths of the major fleets of the world were established according to the following ratio: Britain and the USA 5; Japan 3; France and Italy 1·75. Although Germany was not a signatory to the Washington Treaty, her navy was subject to even more severe limitations: under the terms of the Versailles Treaty of 1919, the construction of armoured ships of more than 10,000 tons standard displacement was prohibited, and in overall size the navy was reduced to the status of a coastal defence force.

The "battleship holiday" encouraged the major navies to focus their immediate attention on the modernisation of the battleships completed during World War I since these vessels would, for the foreseeable future, continue to form the nucleus of each battlefleet. The major lessons of the war had been that future battles would be fought at much longer ranges than had been thought possible at the beginning of the dreadnought era, and that improvements were therefore necessary in fire control and in horizontal protection. Concern about the effects of plunging shells striking ships with relatively lightly armoured decks was reinforced by proposals to develop maritime bomber aircraft which would operate from land bases or from the flight decks of aircraft carriers. Most of the older vessels therefore received additional armour plating above their magazines and machinery spaces during the 1920s. Fire control arrangements were improved, and some casemate guns were removed in favour of anti-aircraft guns.

New Construction

Britain was permitted to build two new 16in (406mm) gun battleships — *Nelson* and *Rodney* — under the terms of the Treaty, but the full effects of the restrictions on new designs were experienced only when construction recommenced in earnest in the late 1920s and early 1930s. The first nation to lay down new capital ships was Germany, which was bound not by the terms of the Washington Treaty but by those of the Treaty of Versailles. The ingenious Deutschland class *Panzerschiffe*, which posed a threat to the mercantile fleets of France and Britain and which easily outgunned the "Treaty cruisers" of those countries, effectively established a minimum speed of 26kt for any new battleship design. Their construction also ensured that France and Italy, whose battlefleets were old and slow, would not accede to the proposal to extend the "battleship holiday" for a further five years, a proposal which was accepted by Britain, the United States and Japan in the London Treaty of 1931. France countered the Deutschlands with a new type of fast battleship, the Dunkerque class, and these ships were in turn countered by the Italians with the 30kt battleships of the Littorio class, which were the first of the new vessels to approach the limits on gun calibre and displacement set by the Washington Treaty.

The British waited until the last possible moment to begin work on new battleships, in the hope that further agreements with the USA and Japan would avoid a new arms race. Britain was in the most difficult position of the three major powers: she could not ignore naval and political developments in Europe, but she was also anxious to secure an agreement which would limit the size and firepower of new Japanese capital ships which might threaten her possessions in the Far East. The United States and Japan, however, were interested only in what the other was doing, and each could afford to wait for developments in the rival navy before ordering new ships. The result was that Britain laid down 14in (356mm) gun battleships in the hope that the other two major

Laid down	Germany	France
1929	*Deutschland*	
1930		
1931	*Admiral Scheer*	
1932	*Admiral Graf Spee*	*Dunkerque*
1933		
1934		*Strasbourg*
1935	*Scharnhorst* *Gneisenau*	*Richelieu*
1936	*Bismarck* *Tirpitz*	*Jean Bart*
1937		
1938		
1939		*Clémenceau*
1940		
1941		

New Battle

Above: The British *Nelson* (seen here firing her secondary armament) and *Rodney* were early victims of the Treaty restrictions.

powers would follow; the US Navy went to 16in (406mm) in the North Carolinas on the strength of rumours about new Japanese battleships; and the Japanese themselves went to 18·1in (460mm) in an attempt to counter superior US numbers by a smaller force of "super-battleships".

One of the big problems facing the major naval powers when they resumed new battleship construction was that the 35,000-ton maximum displacement allowed under the Washington Treaty was no longer adequate to support a main armament of eight or nine 16in (406mm) guns because of

ip Construction in the Prewar Period

Italy	Great Britain	Japan	USA
Littorio			
Vittorio Veneto			
	King George V	Yamato	North Carolina
	Prince of Wales		
	Duke of York		
	Howe		
	Anson		
Roma		Musashi	Washington
Impero			
	Lion		South Dakota
	Temeraire		Massachusetts
			Indiana
		Shinano	Alabama
		No.111	Iowa
			New Jersey
	Vanguard		Missouri
			Wisconsin

new requirements which had not been foreseen at the time the Treaty was drawn up. Adequate protection against 16in (406mm) shell required not only a thick side belt, but also a heavy armoured deck covering the ship's vitals. Moreover, speeds of 21–23kt were no longer considered adequate, and raising this figure to 28–30kt required a phenomenal increase in horsepower: the Marylands of 1921–23 required 29,000ehp to make their maximum speed of 21·5kt; the North Carolinas needed 121,000shp for their 27·5kt; and the 33kt Iowas required 200,000shp. These high figures were easily obtainable using the high-pressure lightweight turbines which had been developed by the late 1930s, but high power still required a long ship with extensive machinery spaces, all of which had to be protected against 16in (406mm) shellfire. This in turn brought with it a substantial increase in displacement. A further factor which complicated design was the need to provide not only an anti-destroyer battery of secondary guns, but a substantial high-angle battery for anti-aircraft fire, together with bulky HA directors (generally four in number) mounted high in the ship. The British, the Americans and the French attempted to combine the low-angle/high-angle functions in a dual-purpose battery, but the guns had to be mounted in armoured power-operated turrets, so weight-saving was minimal.

In the face of problems such as these, designers had either to compromise or to cheat. The British and the Americans endeavoured to keep within Treaty limits, and were compelled to accept less than they would ideally have liked. The British King George Vs were well-armoured but somewhat under-gunned, and were 2kt slower than their European contemporaries. The US Navy's North Carolinas were well armed with nine 16in (406mm) guns, but had protection only against 14in (356mm) shellfire and were also slower than the European battleships. The Italian, French and German 15in (381mm) gun battleships all turned out heavy (38,000–42,000 tons), while the Japanese completely

Below: The US 14in/45cal. Mk 3 mounting of 1914 was considered complex for its time, incorporating as it did a two-stage hoist and loading at any angle of elevation. The triple and quadruple mountings of the interwar period introduced further complexities and frequently suffered reliability problems.

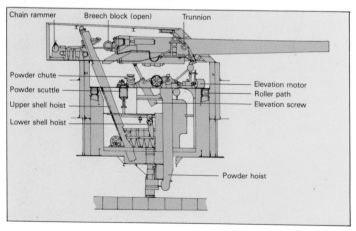

disregarded all Treaty limits with their 63,000-ton battleships of the Yamato class.

Armament

Of the major naval powers, only the United States and Italy had completed battleships with the main guns in triple turrets before 1921. Yet by 1939 the triple turret had become standard, and the French and British were completing battleships with quadruple mountings. Only the more conservative German Navy persisted with the twin mounting. The development of multiple-gun turrets was closely related to the widespread adoption of the "all or nothing" system of protection, which had been introduced by the US Navy in its Nevada class battleships. Multiple-gun turrets were increasingly adopted as a means of compressing the armoured citadel of the battleship, thereby creating considerable economies in weight, and such measures were encouraged by the signing of the Washington Treaty, which placed an upper limit on displacement. In the case of the British King George V class, an additional factor in the adoption of quadruple turrets was the acceptance of an artificially low gun calibre — 14in (356mm) as opposed to 16in (406mm) — for political reasons, which made it necessary to mount twelve (finally ten) main guns. The French, however, favoured the quadruple turret purely for technical and philosophical reasons, and adopted it for all the battleship classes designed in the interwar period.

Multiple-gun turrets did not always live up to the designers' expectations. In the triple turrets the centre gun generally shared a hoist with one or other of the outer guns, which resulted in a lower rate of fire. Both the triple turrets and the quadruple turrets placed a considerable strain on the structure of the ship because of the large openings required for their barbettes, and the enormous recoil forces frequently led to restrictions on the firing of multiple-gun salvos.

Fire control arrangements were steadily improved between the wars in the expectation that the standard range of engagement would increase to

Below: Triple turrets were introduced into the US Navy in 1916 with the Nevada class. They were to become a standard feature of US battleship construction in the interwar period. Here, a battleship of the New Mexico class is seen bombarding the island of Okinawa to "soften up" the Japanese positions, April 1945.

about 25,000yds (23,000m); at Jutland it had generally been 12,000–16,000yds (11,000–14,500m). Longer-base rangefinders were developed, and by the 1930s the directors for the main guns were being installed higher in the ship, generally atop a tower foremast. The most important development of World War II was radar, which effectively divided the world's battlefleets into the "haves" and the "have-nots". In poor weather and poor light conditions the fleet which possessed radar had all the advantages, as the Germans found to their cost when *Scharnhorst* was lost in December 1943.

In older battleships the elevation of the main guns was generally increased to at least 30° during the interwar period to prevent their being outranged by the new vessels under construction, which were faster and could therefore choose the range of engagement (the Italian battlefleet of 1940 was built — or rebuilt — around the principle of "outranging and outrunning").

The 1920s saw the general abandonment of casemates in favour of trainable turrets for the anti-destroyer secondary battery. Casemate guns were limited in elevation (and therefore range), frequently proved unworkable in heavy seas, and required a belt of upper armour which was no longer necessary with the popularity of "all or nothing" schemes of protection. The adoption of turrets for these guns, however, was later to place them in direct competition for deck space with the increasing number of heavy anti-aircraft guns being fitted. The logical solution was the dual-purpose battery, but the development of a successful gun which met all the various requirements was not an easy matter. For anti-aircraft fire a short, lightweight gun was favoured because it was easy to handle and had a high rate of fire, but for accuracy at long range against surface vessels a high muzzle velocity (i.e. a long barrel) was required. Thus the US Navy during the 1920s employed a 5in/51cal (127mm) gun for anti-destroyer work, and a 5in/25cal gun for AA fire. These conflicting requirements could only be resolved by compromise. The 5in/38cal, which finally

Below: The German battleship *Tirpitz* fires her 15in guns during the bombardment of Spitzbergen in September 1943. The Germans continued to favour separate anti-destroyer and anti-aircraft batteries, and here one of *Tirpitz*'s twin 5·9in turrets stands out clearly beneath a twin 4·1in AA mounting.

Right: The modernised US battleship *New Jersey* fires off a Tomahawk surface-to-surface missile. SSMs have now effectively replaced big guns in the anti-ship role, because they are capable of longer range and have precision guidance systems which are independent of the launch ship. Large-calibre guns can, however, still deliver large quantities of ordnance more economically in the fire support/shore bombardment role.

became the standard dual-purpose gun of the US Navy, was generally regarded as a successful anti-aircraft weapon but was considered deficient in anti-surface performance. On the other hand, the corresponding British 5·25in/50cal (133mm) weapon, which was biased towards anti-destroyer work, was less effective in the anti-aircraft role because of its relatively low speeds of training and elevation and low rate of fire.

Apart from the British and the Americans, only the French experimented with the dual-purpose battery. The 5in/45cal (127mm) gun developed for the Dunkerque class proved a conspicuous failure, and was abandoned in the Richelieu class in favour of separate secondary and AA batteries. The German, Japanese and Italian navies persisted throughout with separate heavy anti-destroyer and lighter AA batteries.

War experience established the need for more numerous and effective light AA guns. Most of the weapons developed before 1939 were found to be inadequate, and this led to the widespread adoption of the 40mm Bofors and 20mm Oerlikon gun in the Allied navies. The anti-aircraft fire of Allied battleships was generally more effective than that of their German, Italian and Japanese equivalents because of the provision of radar fire control for all but the smaller weapons.

Protection

With the exception of the German Navy, which was by nature more conservative and which did not have the opportunity to test old hulls to destruction after World War I, all the major navies went over from the complex graduated armour system to "all or nothing" schemes of protection between the wars. Generally speaking these systems comprised a heavy side belt of maximum (and uniform) thickness, with a heavy armoured deck resting on its upper edge to counter plunging shells. This structure was closed at each end by heavy armoured bulkheads, which were located immediately forward and aft of the heavy gun turrets. The only additional protection outside this "citadel" was on the turrets and their barbettes, around the conning tower, and above the steering gear aft, although some navies (notably the US Navy) also favoured light plating at upper deck level to decap armour-piercing shells and detonate bombs before they reached the main armoured deck.

Once engagement ranges increased, the "all or nothing" system was inevitable if the ship's vitals were to be protected against plunging shells, especially on a limited displacement. The only major weakness of the system was that while shells striking outside the armoured citadel were

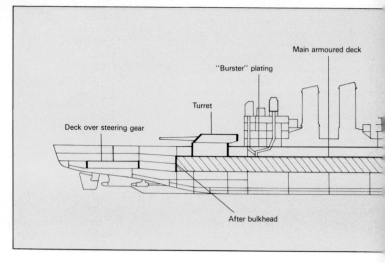

Above: The "all or nothing" protection system of the US battleship *North Carolina*. See main entry for further details.

unlikely to cripple the ship by destroying its propulsion machinery or detonating the magazines, they could seriously threaten buoyancy by blowing large holes in the unarmoured ship's sides, thereby admitting a large volume of water.

Underwater protection was improved considerably between the wars, largely as a result of testing. Bulges were fitted to many vessels, and internal protection generally comprised three or four longitudinal bulkheads with liquid loading in some compartments to distribute the shock wave as evenly as possible. A major

weakness of most battleships was the lack of consideration given to the protection of propeller shafts and rudders. Both *Bismarck* and *Prince of Wales* were crippled by airborne torpedoes which struck in this area; the subsequent loss of speed and manoeuvrability ensured their demise. The "tunnel stern" adopted by the Americans, in which the outer propellers were mounted on large skegs which provided protection for the inner shafts, undoubtedly reduced the vulnerability of US battleships to such damage.

Propulsion

In 1921 the battle fleets of the major navies were expected to steam into action at only 21–22kt, and the upper displacement limit of 35,000 tons established by the Washington Treaty appeared to preclude any change in this

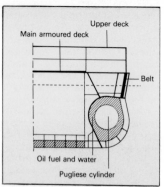

Left: The underwater protection system devised by the Italian engineer Pugliese for the battleships of the Littorio class. It comprised a hollow cylinder of 3·8m (max.) diameter floating in fuel oil. See also main entry.

14

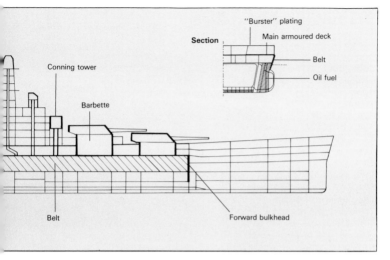

Section

"Burster" plating

Main armoured deck

Belt

Oil fuel

Conning tower

Barbette

Belt

Forward bulkhead

direction. However, the development of lightweight, high-pressure turbines opened up the possibility of genuine fast battleships, as opposed to lightly armoured vessels of the discredited battlecruiser type.

The trend towards high speed in capital ships was begun by the lesser naval powers, who were naturally anxious to engage the battle fleets of the two "super-powers", Britain and the USA, only on their own terms. France and Italy were the first to lay down 30kt battleships, with Germany following close behind. The Royal Navy and the US Navy continued to favour staying power over high performance, but were compelled to raise speeds to 27–28kt to avoid being outrun by the new European battleships.

Lightweight turbines were not only employed in new construction, but were installed in many older battleships in the course of major refits during the 1930s. The Japanese raised the speed of their entire battle fleet to 25–26kt by this method, giving it a 4–5kt advantage over the American fleet. The Italians completely rebuilt the former dread-

noughts of the Cavour and Duilio classes, thereby creating a fleet of modern battleships which completely outclassed the ageing French vessels. The British, on the other hand, preferred to reallocate the weight and space saved by fitting new machinery in the Queen Elizabeths and the battle-cruiser *Renown* to modern batteries of anti-aircraft guns, installed horsepower remaining about the same.

The Germans introduced a significant innovation in battleship propulsion when they installed diesel engines in the Deutschland class. The diesels of the day were bulky, heavy and unreliable, and they were rejected in favour of high-pressure steam turbines in the Scharnhorst and Bismarck classes, but the Germans still hoped to resolve the early problems experienced with this type of propulsion in time to install diesels in the "H" class battleships which were projected to follow *Bismarck* and *Tirpitz*. The principal attraction as compared with steam machinery was low fuel consumption and high endurance, which would have proved invaluable in commerce-raiding operations.

Rivadavia Class

Names: *Rivadavia, Moreno.*
Laid down: 1910.
Completed: 1914–15.
Displacement: 28,000 tons standard; 31,000 tons full load.
Dimensions: Length 585ft (178·3m) oa; beam 95ft (29m); draught 28ft (8·5m).
Propulsion: Curtis steam turbines, 18 Babcock boilers; 45,000shp; 3 shafts; 23kt.
Armour: Belt 11in–4in (280–100mm); decks 1·5in + 3in (38mm + 75mm); barbettes 12in (305mm); turrets 12in–3in (305–75mm); conning tower 12in (305mm).
Armament: 12 x 12in (305mm); 12 x 6in (152mm; 4 x 3in (76mm) AA; 4 x 40mm AA; 2 x 21in (533mm) torpedo tubes.
Complement: 1,050–1,215.

Development: The two battleships of the Rivadavia class were ordered as a response to the construction in Britain of dreadnoughts for Argentina's principal rival, Brazil. *Rivadavia* and *Moreno* were built in the USA, and their design therefore incorporated a number of features which were common to US Navy battleships of the period, but there were also European influences. US Navy influence could be seen in the superimposed turrets fore and aft and in the cage foremast. The arrangement of the two wing turrets was, however, reminiscent of the Royal Navy dreadnoughts of the Neptune and Hercules classes, while the heavy 6in (152mm) secondary battery conformed to German practice. The protection system was generally similar to that of British battleships, but with the addition of bottom armour.

The ships were designed for the relatively high speed of 23kt, and the layout of the propulsion machinery was clearly influenced by that of the Italian *Dante Alighieri.* A three-shaft arrangement was adopted, with the boiler rooms forward and aft of the turbine room, which was located amidships. This arrange-

Above: *Rivadavia* as she appeared after refit in the USA in 1924-25. The former pole mainmast was replaced by a tall tripod, and the anti-aircraft battery was enhanced with the addition of 3in guns.

ment was particularly attractive because of the wide arcs it opened up for the wing turrets.

Both ships were modernised in the USA in 1924–25, when the boilers were converted to oil-burning, the pole mainmast was replaced by a tripod, and 3in (76mm) AA guns were fitted. In 1940 4 x 40mm AA guns were added, but by this time the ships were of limited military value. They were sold for scrap in 1957, having served the Argentine Navy for over forty years.

Below: *Moreno* was similarly modified during the mid-1920s. Both ships were converted to oil-burning, and new fire control directors were fitted atop "B" and "X" turrets.

17

Minas Gerais Class

Names: *Minas Gerais, São Paulo.*
Laid down: 1907.
Completed: 1910.
Displacement: 19,280 tons standard.
Dimensions: Length 533ft (162·4m) oa; beam 83ft (25·3m); draught 25ft (7·6m).
Propulsion: Triple-expansion engines, 18 Babcock boilers in *São Paulo,* 6 Thornycroft boilers in *Minas Gerais;* 23,500/30,000shp; 2 shafts; 21/22kt.
Armour: Belt 9in–4in (230–100mm); decks 2in + 1in (50mm + 25mm); barbettes 9in (230mm); turrets 9in (230mm); conning tower 12in–8in (305–205mm).
Armament: 12 × 12in (305mm); 14/12 × 4·7in (120mm); 4 × 4in (102mm) AA, 4 × 40mm AA in *Minas Gerais,* 2 × 3in (76mm) AA *São Paulo.*
Complement: 850.

Development: Built in Britain, these were the first dreadnoughts ordered by a South American navy and were, when commissioned, the world's most powerful battleships. *Minas Gerais* was modernised in 1934–37, when she was reboilered and received new AA guns. The boiler uptakes were merged into a single broad funnel. A similar conversion was planned for *São Paulo,* but her hull and machinery were in such poor condition that the refit was cancelled; indeed, when the ship was sent for scrapping in 1951 she foundered in the Atlantic Ocean en route for the breaker's in Italy. *Minas Gerais* was broken up in 1954, one of the oldest surviving dreadnoughts.

Almirante Latorre

Laid down: 1911.
Completed: 1915.
Displacement: 28,500 tons standard; 32,500 tons full load.
Dimensions: Length 661ft (201·5m) oa; beam 103ft (31·4m); draught 29ft (8·8m).
Propulsion: Parsons geared steam turbines, 21 Yarrow boilers; 37,000shp; 4 shafts; 22·5kt.
Armour: Belt 9in–4in (230–100mm); decks 1·5in + 4in–1in (38mm + 100–25mm); barbettes 10in–4in (255–100mm); turrets 10in (255mm); conning tower 11in–6in (280–150mm).
Armament: 10 x 14in (356mm); 14 x 6in (152mm); 4 x 4in (102mm) AA; 2 x 40mm AA; 4 x 21in (533mm) torpedo tubes.
Complement: 1,176.

Below: *Almirante Latorre* as HMS *Canada* in 1915. Confiscated by the British while building, she operated with the Grand Fleet from the time of her completion, and she was present at the Battle of Jutland in 1916. She was returned to Chile only in 1920.

Above: *São Paulo* as
completed. In
appearance she
closely resembled
HMS *Dreadnought*.

Below: *Minas Gerais*
as she appeared after
her modernisation in
1934-37.

Development: One of two battleships ordered from Britain in 1911, *Almirante Latorre* served with the British Grand Fleet as *Canada* from her completion until she was returned to Chile in 1920; the second ship was retained by the Royal Navy and was completed as the aircraft carrier *Eagle*. *Almirante Latorre* was modernised in 1929-31, when she was re-engined and had anti-torpedo bulges fitted. The light AA armament was increased during World War II by the addition of 18 x 20mm. She continued to serve in the postwar period, decommissioning in 1958.

Below: *Almirante Latorre* at Devonport for modernisation in 1929-31.
Her boilers were changed to oil-burning and bulges were fitted.

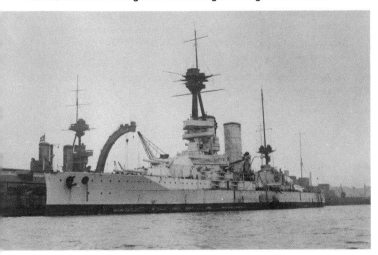

FRANCE
Provence Class

Names: *Provence, Bretagne, Lorraine.*
Laid down: 1912.
Completed: 1915–16.
Displacement: 22,190 tons standard; 26,700–28,500 tons full load.
Dimensions: Length 544ft 6in (166m) oa; beam 88ft 9in (27m); draught 29ft 9in (9·2m).
Propulsion: Parsons steam turbines, 6 Indret boilers; 43,000shp; 4 shafts; 21kt.
Armour: Belt 10·6in–6·3in (270–160mm); decks 1·25in + 1·6in + 2·75in (30mm + 40mm + 70mm); barbettes 10·6in–9·8in (270–250mm); turrets 13·4in–9·75in (340–250mm); conning tower 12·4in (315mm).
Armament: 10/8 x 13·4in (340mm); 14 x 5·5in (138mm); 8 x 3in/3·9in (76/100mm) AA; 4–8 x 37mm AA; 12 x 13·2mm AA. See notes.
Complement: 1,130.

Development: The three old battleships of the Provence class underwent only limited modernisations between the wars. In the first, in 1921–23, the elevation of the main armament was increased from 18⁰ to 23⁰; in the second they were converted to oil burning; and in the third, in 1932–36, they were given new oil-fired boilers and new fire control equipment, the number of guns in the secondary battery was reduced, and anti-aircraft machine guns were fitted. *Lorraine* was more extensively modernised than the others, losing her centre turret to provide a catapult (four spotter aircraft) and a superior AA battery of four twin 3·9in (100mm) mountings.

In September 1939 all three ships were in the Mediterranean. *Lorraine,* supported by a squadron of British cruisers, bombarded Badia in June 1940, and was in Alexandria as flagship of Force "X" when France capitulated. She and the rest of the force were interned until May 1943, when the ships were handed over to the Free French. She subsequently supported the assault on Dakar and the Allied landings in southern France. In 1945 she became a training ship and was hulked.

Bretagne and *Provence* were at Mers-el-Kebir in July 1940. Both were heavily hit by 15in shells from the British capital ships *Hood, Barham* and *Resolution* while still at their moorings, and *Bretagne* capsized after her magazines exploded. *Provence* was set ablaze and sank in shallow water. She was salvaged and returned to Toulon in November 1940, and was scuttled there together with the remains of the French Fleet in November 1942, having been used briefly by the Germans as a floating battery.

Right: *Bretagne* in 1927, following her conversion to oil-burning. The massive tripod foremast was fitted after World War I.

Below: The immediate predecessors of the Provences were the 12in-gun Courbet class. By the early 1930s they had been relegated to training duties. This is *Courbet* in 1938.

Dunkerque Class

Names: *Dunkerque, Strasbourg.*
Laid down: 1932–34.
Completed: 1937–38.
Displacement: 26,500 tons standard; 35,500 tons full load.
Dimensions: Length 703ft 9in (214·5m) oa; beam 102ft 3in (31·1m); draught 31ft 6in (9·6m).
Propulsion: Parsons geared steam turbines, 6 Indret boilers; 112,500shp; 4 shafts; 29·5kt.
Armour: Belt 9·5in–7·7in (240–195mm); decks 5in–4·5in + 1·6in (125–115mm + 40mm); barbettes 13·6in (345mm); turrets 13in–6in (330–150mm); conning tower 10·6–6·3in (270–160mm).
Armament: 8 × 13in (330mm); 16 × 5·1in (130mm) DP; 8 × 37mm AA; 32 × 13·2mm AA.
Complement: 1,381–1,431.

Development: The impetus for the construction of the Dunkerque class was provided by the German Deutschlands. The older French battleships were far too slow to catch the German vessels, so high speed was an important feature of the new vessels, which would in effect be the world's first "fast battleships".

Dunkerque was heavily influenced by the latest British thinking on capital ship design and, like the British Nelsons, had her main armament concentrated forward. The quadruple turrets adopted had been a feature of earlier French designs such as the battleships of the Normandie and Lyon classes and were similarly arranged, with the port and starboard pairs of barrels in each turret

Right: *Dunkerque* **shortly after completion. The design was heavily influenced by that of the British Nelsons, with an all-forward main armament and a turret bridge structure. The system of protection was also similar, although armour thicknesses were adequate only to withstand German 11in shell at a range of 18,000yds. Under-water protection comprised alternate air and fuel compart-ments with a torpedo bulkhead on the inboard side and a com-partment filled with *ébonite mousse* — a rubber-based com-pound — on the outboard side.**

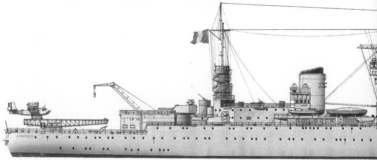

elevating together. The guns were of 13in (330mm) calibre (considered sufficient to defeat the German *Panzerschiffe*) and had a range of 32,800yds (30,000m) at their maximum elevation of 35°.

An important theoretical advantage of the disposition of the main armament in quadruple turrets forward was a reduction in the length of the armoured citadel required. However, in order to avoid the risk of both turrets being put out of action by a single hit, they had to be placed a full 90ft (27m) apart. The major saving was therefore in the weight of the mountings themselves as compared with a more conventional arrangement of four twin turrets.

Dunkerque and *Strasbourg* were the first battleships to have a dual-purpose secondary battery. The twin and quadruple 5·1in (130mm) mountings adopted were not, however, considered to be a success. They were too unwieldy for effective anti-aircraft fire and were prone to frequent breakdowns, and in the Richelieu class which followed the French reverted to separate anti-destroyer and AA batteries. A catapult was fitted, and two aircraft could be carried.

The ships were well designed for their primary mission, that of protecting French merchant shipping from German commerce raiders, but were no match for the fast battleships subsequently laid down by Germany and Italy. Both were deployed in the Atlantic at the outbreak of war and were engaged in the pursuit of *Graf Spee* and *Deutschland*. They were transferred to the Mediterranean in April 1940, and were at Mers-el-Kebir when the British demanded the surrender of the French fleet in July. *Strasbourg* got underway quickly and managed to escape the British blockade, but *Dunkerque* was hit by four 15in shells early in the action and lost all power. She was further damaged in a later aerial attack launched from the carrier *Ark Royal*, when a torpedo struck a patrol boat moored alongside, causing depth charges to explode. By February 1942 she had been patched up sufficiently to return to Toulon, and in November she was scuttled together with her sister *Strasbourg*.

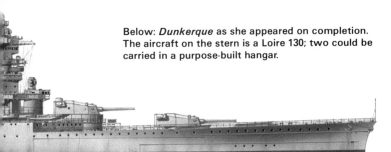

Below: *Dunkerque* as she appeared on completion. The aircraft on the stern is a Loire 130; two could be carried in a purpose-built hangar.

Richelieu Class

Names: *Richelieu, Jean Bart, Clémenceau.*
Laid down: 1935–39.
Completed: 1940–55.
Displacement: 35,000 tons standard; 44,000 tons full load.
Dimensions: Length 813ft 2in (247·9m) oa; beam 108ft 3in (33m); draught 31ft 7in (9·6m).
Propulsion: Parsons geared steam turbines, 6 Indret Sural boilers; 150,000shp; 4 shafts; 30kt.
Armour: Belt 13·6in–9·75in (345–250mm); decks 6·75in–6in + 1·6in (170–150mm + 40mm); barbettes 16in (405mm); turrets 17in–7·7in (430–195mm); conning tower 13·4in–6·75in (340–170mm).
Armament: 8 x 15in (380mm); 9 x 6in (152mm); 12 x 3·9in (100mm) AA; 8 x 37mm AA; 16 x 13·2mm AA.
Complement: 1,550.

Development: The construction by Italy of two battleships armed with 15in (381mm) guns compelled the French to follow suit. Design work began in 1934, and a main armament of twelve guns of 13·4in (340mm) or 13·8in (350mm) calibre in quadruple turrets was considered before the final decision was made in favour of eight 15in (381mm) guns.

As initially designed, *Richelieu* was essentially an enlarged *Dunkerque*, the similarities extending to a large single funnel placed well abaft the turret bridge structure, the layout of the secondary armament (which was originally to com-

Above: *Richelieu* **photographed from HMS** *Anson* **in 1945 during the period of service with the British Eastern Fleet.**

prise five triple 6in (152mm) turrets), and the aircraft-handling arrangements (two catapults, three aircraft) on the stern. The protection system was also identical, although armour thicknesses were substantially increased in order to resist 15in (381mm) shells. Total armour weight was 16,400 tons, or 37 per cent of displacement (an identical figure to *Dunkerque*). ▶

Below: *Richelieu* **enters New York harbour in early 1943, prior to a major refit in which she was to receive a new AA armament.**

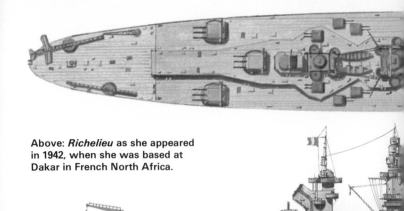

Above: *Richelieu* as she appeared in 1942, when she was based at Dakar in French North Africa.

During construction a number of important modifications were made. The funnel was combined with the after director tower, the exhaust gases being led aft through an angled vent. This kept the director tower free of smoke, and greater optical height was obtained without additional weight. It was decided to dispense with the midships 6in (152mm) turrets in favour of additional anti-aircraft weapons. Twelve 3·9in (100mm) guns were grouped close together amidships, and there were to be eight twin 37mm mountings. This was a comparatively weak AA armament by contemporary foreign standards, and most of the wartime and postwar modifications to the ships were focused on this area.

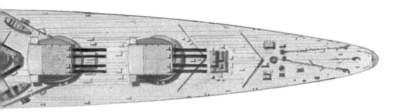

Below: As first completed *Richelieu* had aircraft-handling arrangements on the stern as did the Dunkerque class. The aircraft is a Loire 130.

Richelieu was nearly complete when France capitulated in June 1940, and the ship escaped to Dakar. *Jean Bart,* which had been launched only in March, escaped from St. Nazaire to Casablanca. In July 1940 *Richelieu* was attacked by aircraft from the British carrier *Hermes.* She was struck by a torpedo beneath the stern, and sank in shallow water. In September 1940 she was subjected to further attacks by the British, and engaged in a gun battle with the battleship *Resolution.* She finally went over to the Free French, and from February to August 1943 was extensively refitted at New York Navy Yard. The aircraft catapults were removed from the stern and a powerful AA armament, comprising 14 quadruple 40mm mountings and 14 (later 50) 20mm guns, was ▶

Left: The massive quadruple turrets of *Richelieu* are trained to starboard during operations with the British Eastern Fleet. The 40mm mountings were fitted during the ship's US refit.

Below: The 15in gun barrels of "A" turret aboard *Richelieu,* seen here in 1947. The barrels could not be elevated independently; each pair was located in a common mounting.

fitted. *Richelieu* subsequently served with the British Eastern Fleet until the end of the war, when she remained in French Indo-China. She returned to Cherbourg in 1946, and ten years later was placed in reserve.

Jean Bart, still lacking many of her guns and her fire control equipment, was attacked by US naval forces in November 1942. She was hit by eight 16in (406mm) shells from the battleship *Massachusetts* and set ablaze. She remained in Casablanca until the end of the war, when she was moved to Brest for completion. This was delayed for a time by a shortage of funds, but in 1952 she finally emerged with a completely revised AA armament of 24 x 3·9in (100mm) and 28 x 57mm guns in twin mountings. She was present at Suez in 1956, but decommissioned in 1961.

Clémenceau, the third ship of the class, was laid down only in January 1939. Her construction was not far advanced when France capitulated, and all work on her ceased from that date.

Right: After World War II *Richelieu* was employed as a training ship. Note the triple turrets of the secondary armament.

Below: *Richelieu* as she appeared in 1953, largely unmodified since World War II. The 20mm guns had by this time been removed, but she retained her quadruple 40mm guns. Note the British-type radars.

Deutschland Class

Names: *Deutschland, Admiral Scheer, Admiral Graf Spee.*
Laid down: 1929–32.
Completed: 1933–36.
Displacement: 11,700–12,100 tons standard; 15,900–16,200 tons full load.
Dimensions: Length 610ft 3in (186m) oa; beam 67ft 7in–70ft 10in (20·6–21·6m); draught 23ft 7in–24ft 3in (7·2–7·4m).
Propulsion: 8 MAN diesels; 54,000bhp; 2 shafts; 28kt.
Armour: Belt 3·2in–2·4in (80–60mm) in *Graf Spee,* 2·4in–2in (60–50mm) in others; deck 1·8in–1·6in (45–40mm); barbettes 4in (100mm); turrets 5·5in–3·3in (140–85mm); conning tower 6in–2in (150–50mm).
Armament: 6 x 11in (280mm); 8 x 5·9in (150mm); 6 x 3·5/4·1in (88/105mm) AA; 8 x 37mm AA; 8 x 21in (533mm) torpedo tubes.
Complement: 1,000–1,150.

Development: The design of the Deutschland class was undoubtedly the most ingenious and controversial of the interwar period. Germany was limited by the terms of the Treaty of Versailles to ships of 10,000 tons standard displacement — a move intended to preclude further capital ship construction. There was, however, no corresponding limit on major gun calibre, so the German designers opted for a ship that would possess a gun armament superior to that of any cruiser — and the speed to outrun any battleship.

Above: *Admiral Graf Spee* was more heavily armoured than her two sisters. She had a turret foremast similar to that of *Admiral Sheer,* from which she could be distinguished by her taller topmast. She was sunk before any modifications could be carried out.

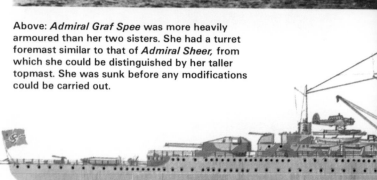

Above: The "pocket battleship" *Admiral Graf Spee* **photographed shortly before the outbreak of World War II.**

The main 11in (280mm) guns were disposed forward and aft in two triple turrets, and were backed up by eight 5·9in (150mm) guns in single mountings on the beam. A modern AA armament on the scale of contemporary cruiser construction was fitted, and above-decks torpedo tubes were mounted for commerce raiding. There was one catapult, with two aircraft.

The armour was also of cruiser standard, being designed to cope with 8in (203mm) shellfire. Because of the constraints on displacement, the armoured ▶

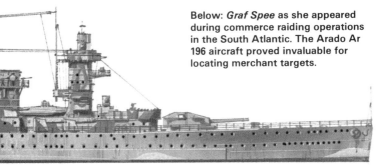

Below: *Graf Spee* **as she appeared during commerce raiding operations in the South Atlantic. The Arado Ar 196 aircraft proved invaluable for locating merchant targets.**

deck of the first two units did not extend to the ships' sides but was terminated at the upper edge of the inclined torpedo bulkhead. The third ship, *Graf Spee,* was slightly larger, and the increase in beam made it possible to extend the armoured deck outwards to join the side belt, which was thicker and deeper than that of her sisterships. Electric welding was employed extensively in the construction of all three vessels, resulting in savings of 15 per cent in the weight of the hull alone.

The Deutschlands were unique among interwar capital ships in having diesel propulsion. Marine diesels were then in their infancy, and those adopted for the Deutschland class were heavy, space-consuming (especially in terms of ►

Left: *Deutschland* astern of *Admiral Graf Spee* in 1939. By this time the former had received a number of modifications, including a flat, inclined funnel cowling, a new mainmast with aerial spreaders, and armoured covers for the torpedo tubes.

Below: *Admiral Graf Spee* following her scuttling off Montevideo in December 1939. Harassed by the cruisers *Exeter, Ajax* and *Achilles,* the German vessel took shelter in neutral Uruguay to carry out temporary repairs and to replenish her stores. The scheduled break-out was abandoned after the British spread rumours about a large allied naval force lying in wait off the mouth of the River Plate.

height), and prone to frequent breakdowns in service. They were, however, responsible for the considerable range of these ships, which made them eminently suited to commerce raiding.

In August 1939 *Deutschland* and *Admiral Graf Spee* were positioned in the North and South Atlantic respectively in anticipation of the outbreak of war. *Deutschland* sank two merchant ships and captured a third before returning to Germany. *Graf Spee* was more successful, sinking nine ships of 50,089grt in the South Atlantic and the Indian Ocean before being intercepted by the British cruisers *Exeter, Ajax* and *Achilles* in December. Following the Battle of the River Plate, in which she received some damage, she entered Montevideo harbour and was subsequently scuttled.

Deutschland was renamed *Lützow* in November 1939, and the surviving two units of the class were redesignated "heavy cruisers" in February 1940 (they were previously referred to as *Panzerschiffe,* or "armoured ships"). *Lützow* took part in the German occupation of Norway in April 1940. She was heavily engaged by Norwegian coastal batteries in Oslofjord and sustained three 11in (280mm) shell hits. While returning to Germany she was struck by a torpedo from the British submarine *Spearfish,* and was subsequently under repair until January 1941. While attempting to break out into the North Atlantic in July, she was struck by an airborne torpedo which put her in dockyard hands again until January 1942.

Admiral Scheer began the war with serious machinery problems, which kept her in dock until September 1940. In October she sortied into the North Atlantic, where she attacked convey HX84, sinking the auxiliary cruiser *Jervis Bay* and six merchantmen. She returned to Kiel in April 1941, having sunk 17 ships totalling 113,233grt. A planned breakout into the North Atlantic with the new battleship *Tirpitz* in November 1941 was cancelled because of a perceived threat to Norway. In February 1942 *Admiral Scheer* was transferred to Trondheim, and in May was, with *Lützow,* moved to Narvik to threaten the Murmansk convoys. Both ships sortied against convoys PQ17 and QP13 (Operation *Rösselsprung*) in July, but the operation was abandoned when *Lützow* and three destroyers ran aground. *Admiral Scheer* returned to Germany for refit in November 1942, but *Lützow* took part in the disastrous action against convoy JW51B near Bear Island in December of that year. Hitler's increasing displeasure with the performance of the German Navy's major surface vessels resulted in the withdrawal of both *Lützow* and *Scheer* from active service during 1943, but in late 1944 both were brought back from their premature retire-

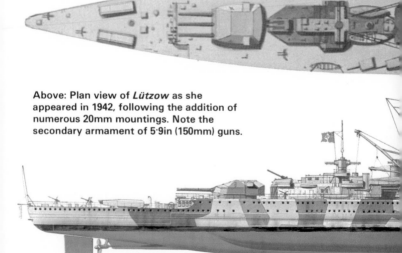

Above: Plan view of *Lützow* as she appeared in 1942, following the addition of numerous 20mm mountings. Note the secondary armament of 5·9in (150mm) guns.

Above: *Lützow* (formerly *Deutschland*) at anchor behind anti-torpedo net and boom defences in a Norwegian fjord. From May 1942 she and *Admiral Scheer* were based at Narvik to threaten the Murmansk convoys, but after the disastrous action against convoy JW51 off Bear Island both ships were withdrawn from active service.

ment to provide fire support against the approaching Soviet armies in the Baltic. In April 1945 *Lützow* was attacked south of Swinemünde by British bombers with 12,000lb (5,440kg) bombs. Heavily damaged by near-misses, she settled on the bottom and was employed thereafter as a stationary gun battery. In the same month *Admiral Scheer*, undergoing refit at Kiel, was hit by five bombs and capsized.

Both *Lützow* and *Scheer* received extensive wartime modifications. Cowlings were added to the funnels, and a new modified bow, with increased sheer, was fitted to improve sea-keeping. Additional anti-aircraft guns were installed: 6 x 40mm and 26 x 20mm in *Lützow,* and 6 x 40mm and 24 x 20mm in *Scheer.*

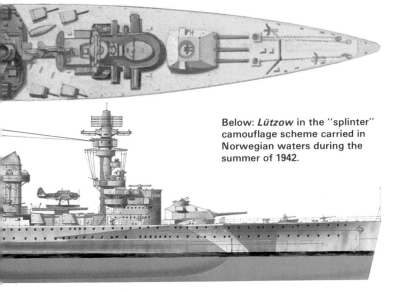

Below: *Lützow* in the "splinter" camouflage scheme carried in Norwegian waters during the summer of 1942.

GERMANY
Scharnhorst Class

Names: *Scharnhorst, Gneisenau.*
Laid down: 1935.
Completed: 1938–39.
Displacement: 31,850 tons standard; 38,900 tons full load.
Dimensions: Length 770ft 8in (234·9m) oa; beam 98ft 5in (30m); draught 32ft 6in (9·9m).
Propulsion: Brown-Boveri/Germania geared steam turbines, 12 Wagner boilers; 160,000shp; 3 shafts; 31·5kt.
Armour: Belt 13·8in–8in (350–200mm); decks 2in + 2in (50mm + 50mm); barbettes 13·8in–8in (350–200mm); turrets 14in–6in (360–150mm); conning tower 13·8in-4in (350–100mm).
Armament: 9 x 11in (280mm); 12 x 5·9in (150mm); 14 x 4·1in (105mm) AA; 16 x 37mm AA; 10 x 20mm AA.
Complement: 1,840.

Development: The construction by the French of the two fast battleships of the Dunkerque class invalidated the principles which served as the basis of the Deutschland design. The fourth and fifth ships of the latter class were therefore cancelled in favour of a larger and more powerful design which could match the French vessels. The result was the two ships of the Scharnhorst class. In protection and speed they were to be more than a match for *Dunkerque* and *Strasbourg,* but the main armament was the subject of some debate. Some German naval officers felt that guns of 14in (356mm) or 15in (380mm) calibre were needed to counter the 13in (330mm) guns of the French ships, while others continued to favour the 11in (280mm) gun because of its high rate of fire. The eventual decision in favour of the 11in gun was largely political, because it was felt that the adoption of a higher calibre would antagonise the British, with whom an Anglo-German naval agreement was in the process of being negotiated.

Above: *Gneisenau* on builders' trials in the spring of 1938. As completed she and *Scharnhorst* had a straight stem; following sea trials it was decided to fit a clipper stem, but the vessels continued to ship water over "A" turret in heavy seas.

A newly developed armour plating steel suitable for electric welding was used in the ships' construction. The protection system adopted was essentially that of the Mackensen and Ersatz Yorck battlecruiser designs of World War I, with burster armour on the upper deck and upper sides and a low main armoured deck covering the ships' vitals. Armour accounted for some 40 per cent of displacement.

Diesel propulsion, as in the Deutschland class, was originally planned, but this proposal had to be abandoned because of the exceptionally high power per shaft needed to drive the ships at their maximum designed speed of 32kt. High-pressure superheated steam machinery was adopted instead; it was lighter and required less space, but proved difficult to maintain. ▶

Below: Another view of *Gneisenau* in 1938. Two aircraft catapults were originally fitted, but the after one was removed in 1940.

Right: *Scharnhorst* received similar modifications to her sister in the summer of 1939, but in addition the mainmast was moved some 88ft further aft. She was given a larger aircraft hangar amidships from the outset. In this view she retains the second catapult on "Y" turret, which was removed in 1940.

Below: The forward turrets of *Gneisenau* are trained to port during sea trials in 1938. The 11in (280mm) calibre was adopted in order not to antagonise the British.

Left: *Gneisenau* in late 1938 after being fitted with an "Atlantic" bow and a prominent funnel cap. She could be distinguished from her sister *Scharnhorst* by the position of the mainmast, which was stepped immediately abaft the funnel. She retained a second catapult atop the after turret until 1940.

Separate secondary and anti-aircraft batteries were maintained, and both were on a par with contemporary foreign battleship construction. Torpedo tubes, however, were not fitted until 1941, when triple 21in (533mm) tubes were installed for commerce raiding. At the same time the close-range AA armament was boosted by the addition of 12–24 x 20mm guns.

Both ships were originally completed with a straight stem, but it was found that they shipped a lot of water over the bows in a seaway, and in 1938–39 a new clipper stem was fitted. This did not entirely solve the problem, which was essentially one of low freeboard, and water was still shipped over "A" turret in heavy seas. At the same time a cowling was added to the funnel, and *Scharnhorst* had her mainmast removed from its original position immediately abaft the funnel and re-sited some 88ft (27m) farther aft. Each ship originally had two aircraft catapults, but that on "Y" turret was later removed. Four aircraft could be carried.

Unlike the Deutschland class, which were generally deployed in independent anti-commerce operations, *Scharnhorst* and *Gneisenau* frequently worked together as fleet units. Although designed to face capital ships, however, they were heavily outgunned by even the older British battleships, and always declined action when the latter were encountered.

In a North Atlantic sortie in November 1939, *Scharnhorst* and *Gneisenau* sank the British auxiliary cruiser *Rawalpindi*. In April 1940 they formed the main spearhead for the occupation of Norway. In a brief action with the battle-cruiser *Renown*, *Gneisenau* sustained three 15in (381mm) shell hits, one of which put her main fire control director out of action, before the German vessels escaped using their superior speed. In June they encountered the British carrier *Glorious*, and sank her along with her two accompanying destroyers. *Scharnhorst* was struck by a torpedo from *Acasta*, however, and ▶

entered Trondheim with 2,500 tons of water inside her. *Gneisenau* was subsequently struck by a torpedo from the submarine *Clyde*. Both ships were under repair until late 1940, when they attempted an unsuccessful breakout into the North Atlantic.

In January 1941 they met with greater success, and in a foray which lasted until March sank 22 ships totalling 115,000grt. They subsequently entered Brest, where they received the full attention of the Royal Air Force. In April *Gneisenau* was struck by a torpedo and four bombs, while *Scharnhorst* received five bomb hits. It was decided that they should return to Germany via the English Channel, in company with the cruiser *Prinz Eugen*. The "Channel Dash", as it subsequently became known, took place in February 1942. The escape was successful, but both *Scharnhorst* and *Gneisenau* struck mines off the Dutch coast. While under repair at Kiel *Gneisenau* was crippled by heavy bombs and her entire forecastle was destroyed. It was planned to refit her with three twin 15in (380mm) turrets, but she was never to see service again.

Scharnhorst was transferred to Norway in March 1943. She sortied against convoy JB55B in December, but in the Battle of North Cape she was hounded by cruiser and destroyer attacks and finally sunk by the battleship *Duke of York*.

Below: *Scharnhorst* as she appeared during "Operation Cerberus" — the "Channel Dash" from Brest to Kiel in company with *Gneisenau* and *Prinz Eugen*.

Above: *Gneisenau* at sea during World War II. The camouflage scheme suggests that the photo dates from late 1940 or early 1941, and was taken from *Scharnhorst* during an Atlantic sortie.

Above: *Gneisenau* leads *Scharnhorst* out of a northern port for a sortie against Allied shipping in the Atlantic. Between January and March 1941 they sank 22 ships totalling 115,000grt. They subsequently entered Brest, where they were heavily bombed by the RAF.

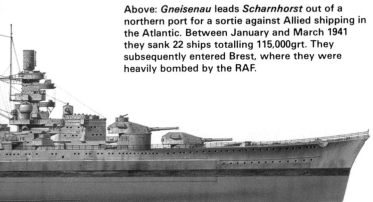

Bismarck Class

Names: *Bismarck, Tirpitz.*
Laid down: 1936.
Completed: 1940–41.
Displacement: 41,700/42,900 tons standard; 50,900/52,600 tons full load.
Dimensions: Length 823ft 6in (251m) oa; beam 118ft 1in (36m); draught 33ft 6in/34ft 10in (10·2/10·6m).
Propulsion: Blohm & Voss/Brown-Boveri geared steam turbines, 12 Wagner boilers; 138,000shp; 3 shafts; 29kt.
Armour: Belt 12·6in–8·7in (320–220mm); decks 2in + 3·2in–4·7in (50mm + 80–120mm); barbettes 13·5in–8·7in (340–220mm); turrets 14·1in–7in (360–180mm); conning tower 13·8in–8·7in (350–220mm).
Armament: 8 x 15in (380mm); 12 x 5·9in (150mm); 16 x 4·1in (105mm) AA; 16 x 37mm AA; 12 x 20mm AA.
Complement: 2,092/2,608.

Development: *Bismarck* and *Tirpitz* were the first and last fully-fledged battleships to be built in Nazi Germany. Design work had been in progress since 1932, and in 1934 development of a new 15in (380mm) gun was begun. *Bismarck* was ordered as soon as the Anglo-German naval agreement was concluded in 1935, and the order for *Tirpitz* followed a year later. France was still seen as Germany's potential naval opponent, and the characteristics of the new German battleships were strikingly similar to those of the French *Richelieu:* both types had a main armament of eight 15in (380mm) guns, a secondary battery of 5·9in/6in (150/152mm) guns, a separate anti-aircraft battery, heavy protection, and a maximum speed of about 30kt.

The basic designs of these two classes were, however, very different. The *Richelieu* was very much a product of the latest thinking on capital ship design, with her big guns concentrated in two quadruple turrets forward, a tower bridge structure, and protection on the "all or nothing" principle. The design for the Bismarck class, on the other hand, could hardly have been more conservative. The main guns were distributed forward and aft in twin turrets according to traditional practice, and the protection system was basically that of the earlier Baden class (completed in 1916), albeit with a slight reduction in the thickness of the side belt and a corresponding increase in horizontal protection.

The Germans, unlike the victors in World War I, had no opportunity to experiment by testing elderly battleship hulls to destruction in the interwar period, and they therefore persisted with the system of protection which had served them so well at Jutland. However, the range at which engagements

Above: *Bismarck* shortly after completion. Note the ridge formed by the upper edge of the 12·6in main armour belt. The two large cranes handled both the ship's boats and the four aircraft.

were likely to take place had increased considerably during the interwar period, and although the new German battleships were well armoured against shells fired at relatively short range, they were more vulnerable to plunging shells than their foreign counterparts. The main armoured deck was placed much lower than those of contemporary foreign vessels, leaving many important compartments, particularly those housing the ships' communications and data systems, exposed to shells which penetrated the lightly armoured upper deck. Nevertheless, *Bismarck* and *Tirpitz* were strongly built and well subdivided, and both proved difficult to sink. Their exceptionally broad beam provided the necessary space for a good system of underwater protection, and also made them very steady gun platforms.

As with *Scharnhorst*, diesel propulsion was out of the question because of the power-per-shaft requirement. Initially turbo-electric propulsion on the US Navy pattern was seriously considered, but there was concern about the vulnerability of the power transmission by cables from the gears to the pro- ▶

Below: *Bismarck* on builders' trials in 1940. She still lacks fire control directors for her main and secondary batteries; these would be located atop the conning tower and the tower foremast, and abaft the mainmast. A boat is being hoisted out amidships.

peller shafts, and it was eventually decided to revert to the high-pressure superheated steam plant of *Scharnhorst* and *Gneisenau*.

The original profile of *Bismarck* as designed was close to that of *Scharnhorst* as she was initially completed, but modifications were subsequently made to the aircraft handling arrangements, which were modelled on those of contemporary British construction and involved a single catapult and 4–6 aircraft, and to the upperworks. A funnel cowling was added, and an "Atlantic" bow was fitted during construction. The original design displacement of 35,000 tons conformed to Treaty limits, but the modifications made while building raised the standard displacement to around 42,000 tons.

Bismarck spent a full year working up before undertaking her first (and final) sortie into the North Atlantic. Accompanied by the cruiser *Prinz Eugen*, she left Korsfjord, Norway, in May 1941, and was intercepted by the battlecruiser *Hood* and the new battleship *Prince of Wales* south of the Denmark Strait. Her fifth salvo sank *Hood*, and she inflicted severe damage on *Prince of Wales* ▶

Left: *Bismarck* at speed. The low free-board of the German battleships caused them to ship large quantities of water over the bows.

Below: *Bismarck* at anchor in Korsfjord, Norway, in May 1941, shortly before her break-out into the North Atlantic in company with the cruiser *Prinz Eugen*.

Right: The sinking of the *Bismarck,* 27 May 1941. Her rudders jammed after a hit by an airborne torpedo, she was unable to manoeuvre, and the heavy firepower of the British battle-ships *King George V* and *Rodney* soon took effect. She nevertheless proved difficult to sink.

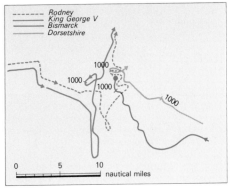

Rodney
King George V
Bismarck
Dorsetshire

1000
1000
1000
1000

0   5   10
nautical miles

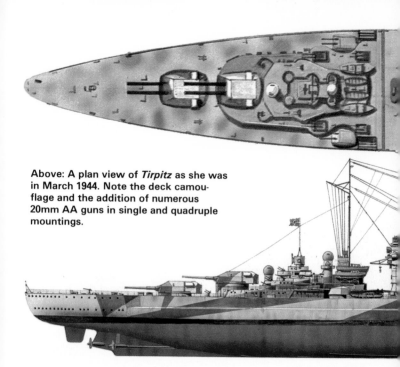

Above: A plan view of *Tirpitz* as she was
in March 1944. Note the deck camouflage and the addition of numerous
20mm AA guns in single and quadruple
mountings.

before the latter was forced to break off the action. She was, however, hit by
three 14in (356mm) shells from *Prince of Wales*, and with oil leaking from a
damaged fuel tank she separated from her consort and headed for Brest to join
Scharnhorst and *Gneisenau*. She subsequently became the focus of attention
for large numbers of British warships, but would undoubtedly have escaped
had she not been struck by a torpedo launched by an aircraft from the carrier
Ark Royal, which crippled her steering and delivered her to the battleships *King
George V* and *Rodney*. She sank after absorbing considerable punishment.

The career of her sister, *Tirpitz*, was less distinguished. Following the
cancellation of a similar North Atlantic sortie planned for November 1941, she
was transferred to Norway and deployed against the Murmansk convoys. In
September 1943 she was heavily damaged by mines laid beneath her keel by
British midget submarines. Then in April 1944, when repairs had only just been
completed, she was hit by 14 bombs delivered by British carrier aircraft and
seriously damaged. She continued thereafter to be subjected to constant air
attacks, and was struck by two bombs from carrier aircraft in August. In
September she was near-missed by a 10,000lb (4,540kg) bomb delivered by
RAF bombers flying from Northern Russia and was never again seaworthy. In
October 1944 she was moved to Tromsö to be used as a floating battery; by
this time she carried a close-range armament of 40 x 20mm in single and
quadruple mountings. In November an attack by 36 RAF Lancaster bombers
armed with 12,000lb (5,440kg) bombs resulted in three direct hits and several
near-misses, and *Tirpitz* capsized.

Right above: *Tirpitz* at anchor in a Norwegian fjord, protected by anti-
torpedo nets. She continued to pose a major threat to the Murmansk
convoys as late as mid-1944, but she had by then become the focus of
attention for carrier- and land-based aircraft, and she sustained heavy
damage in successive attacks.

Right: the upturned hull of *Tirpitz* at Tromsö, after the final attack by
Lancasters of 617 Squadron on 12 November 1944.

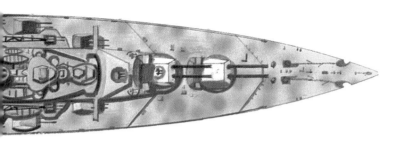

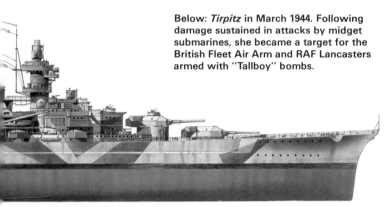

Below: *Tirpitz* in March 1944. Following damage sustained in attacks by midget submarines, she became a target for the British Fleet Air Arm and RAF Lancasters armed with "Tallboy" bombs.

Royal Sovereign Class

Names: *Revenge, Resolution, Ramillies, Royal Oak, Royal Sovereign.*
Laid down: 1913–14.
Completed: 1916–17.
Displacement: 29,150 tons standard; 33,500 tons full load.
Dimensions: Length 620ft 6in (189·2m) oa; beam 101ft 4in–102ft 1in (30·9–31·2m); draught 32ft 10in (9·9m).
Propulsion: Parsons direct drive steam turbines, 18 Yarrow/Babcock & Wilcox boilers; 40,000shp; 4 shafts; 21–22kt.
Armour: Belt 13in–4in (330–100mm); decks 1in + 5in–3·5in (25mm + 125–90mm) in *Royal Oak,* 1in + 1·25in + 2in (25mm + 30mm + 50mm) in others; barbettes 10in–4in (255–100mm); turrets 13in–4·5in (330–115mm); conning tower 11in (280mm).
Armament: 8 x 15in (381mm); 12 x 6in (152mm); 8 x 4in (102mm) AA; 16 x 2pdr; 8 x 0·5in (12·7mm) AA.
Complement: 1,009.

Above: *Royal Sovereign* ahead of *Resolution* and *Revenge* in the North Sea during World War I, when they were the most modern British battleships. They were, however, considered too small and too slow to merit major reconstruction during the interwar period.

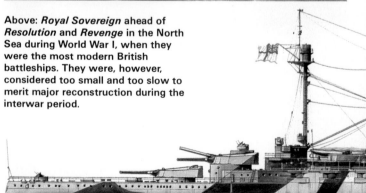

Above: *Resolution* in the Indian Ocean in 1942. The "R" class battleships were the backbone of British Eastern Fleet at this time.

Development: The five battleships of the "R" class were not modernised in the interwar period: smaller and slower than the Queen Elizabeth class, they received only a few token updates, which involved the fitting of anti-torpedo bulges in the 1920s, and modern AA weapons during the 1930s. *Resolution* and *Royal Oak* were fitted with a catapult (one aircraft).

The outbreak of war saw all five ships relegated to second-line duties, as guardships in the English Channel and as convoy escorts for troopships in the Atlantic. *Royal Oak* was sunk during this period, being struck by at least two torpedoes from *U47*, which succeeded in penetrating the fleet anchorage at Scapa Flow. With the entry of Italy into the war in May 1940, *Ramillies* and *Royal Sovereign* were transferred to the Mediterranean Fleet. *Resolution* joined Force "H" at Gibraltar and participated in the operations against the French fleet at Mers-el-Kebir and then at Dakar, where she was torpedoed by the submarine *Bévéziers*. Repairs took until April 1942, by which time the remaining ships of the class had been transferred to the Indian Ocean to form a new Eastern Fleet. In May 1942 *Ramillies* was torpedoed by a Japanese midget submarine while taking part in the operation against Diego Suarez (Madagascar). She rejoined the Eastern Fleet in September 1943.

By late 1943 the balance at sea had swung heavily in favour of the Allies, and all four surviving ships returned to the UK. *Revenge* and *Resolution* became depot ships, being joined by *Ramillies* after her deployment in support of the Allied landings in Normandy and southern France. In August 1944 *Royal Sovereign* was transferred on loan to the Soviet Navy; she was renamed *Arkhangelsk,* and served until 1948, when she was returned to the UK. The four vessels were all sold for scrapping during the late 1940s.

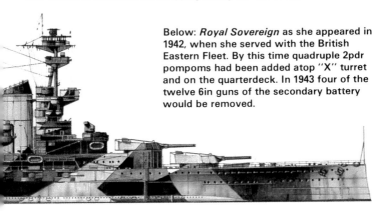

Below: *Royal Sovereign* as she appeared in 1942, when she served with the British Eastern Fleet. By this time quadruple 2pdr pompoms had been added atop "X" turret and on the quarterdeck. In 1943 four of the twelve 6in guns of the secondary battery would be removed.

Queen Elizabeth Class

Names: *Queen Eiizabeth, Warspite, Barham, Valiant, Malaya.*
Laid down: 1912–13.
Completed: 1915–16.
Reconstructed: 1934–37 (*Warspite*), 1937–41 (*Valiant, Queen Elizabeth*).
Displacement: 31,320–31,600 tons standard; 35,380–36,500 tons full load.
Dimensions: Length 644ft (196·3m) oa; beam 90ft 6in (27·6m); draught 33ft 6in–34ft (10·1–10·2m).
Propulsion: Parsons/Brown-Curtis direct-drive steam turbines, 24 Yarrow/Babcock & Wilcox boilers in *Barham, Malaya;* Parsons geared turbines, 6/8 Admiralty boilers in reconstructed ships; 75,000–80,000shp; 4 shafts; 22·5–23·5kt.
Armour: Belt 13in–4in (330–100mm); deck 5in–3·5in (125–90mm); barbettes 10in–4in (255–100mm); turrets 13in–4·25in (330–110mm); conning tower 11in (280mm) in *Barham,* 5in (125mm) in *Malaya,* 3in–2in (75–50mm) in others.
Armament: 8 x 15in (381mm); 12 x 6in (152mm) in *Barham, Malaya,* 8 x 6in (152mm) in *Warspite;* 20 x 4·5in (114mm) DP in *Valiant, Queen Elizabeth,* 8 x 4in (102mm) AA in others; 16/24/32 x 2pdr AA; 16 x 0·5in (12·7mm) AA.
Complement: 1,124.

Development: The Queen Elizabeths were the world's first "fast battleships", and were arguably the most well-balanced capital ships of World War I. They were therefore primary candidates for modernisation during the interwar period. All five ships received anti-torpedo bulges and had their twin funnels trunked together in the 1920s, and in the 1930s they were taken in hand for more fundamental updating.

Barham, the first to undergo a major refit (1931–34), received an additional 500 tons of deck armour, giving her a maximum thickness of 5in (125mm) over the magazines. She also received two high-angle directors and was fitted with a tripod mainmast. She was later to receive a modern anti-aircraft armament, but remained otherwise unmodified.

Malaya was the next to be taken in hand (1934–36), and her refit represented a half-way stage between the minimal modifications given to *Barham* and the later reconstructions. She was given additional protection over the engine

Right: *Malaya* as she appeared in 1934, just before her last major refit. The effects of earlier modifications can be seen in the broad single funnel, the prominent anti-torpedo bulges, and the rebuilt bridge structure. In the refit of 1934-37 she would be fitted with a catapult and twin hangars amidships, and would receive a new anti-aircraft armament of twin 4in guns and 8-barrelled 2pdr pompoms; two high-angle fire control directors would also be fitted.

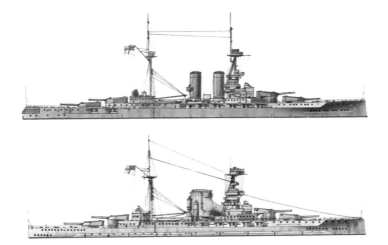

Above: The upper drawing is of *Queen Elizabeth* as completed in 1915, with twin funnels and twenty 6in guns. The lower drawing shows the same ship in 1935, with the boiler uptakes trunked together into a single funnel and with a modified bridge.

rooms, and a cross-deck catapult and hangars were installed. She also received modern AA weapons and HA directors. Neither she nor *Barham*, however, had the elevation of their 15in guns raised beyond the original 20° maximum. This placed them at some disadvantage when they were faced with the new and reconstructed Italian battleships in the Mediterranean in 1940; they even found themselves outranged by the 6in (152mm) secondary armament of the Littorios! They also retained their original machinery, which meant that they rarely exceeded 22kt during World War II.

With the proliferation of new battleship construction in Europe in the early 1930s it was decided that the remaining three units of the class should be totally rebuilt. *Warspite*, the prototype conversion (1934–37), was given new machinery, and the space and weight thus saved was utilised to provide additional horizontal protection, a new "tower" bridge structure modelled on that of *Nelson*, a cross-deck catapult and hangars (three aircraft), and much-▶

improved fire-control arrangements. The original 24 Yarrow large-tube boilers were replaced by six Admiralty boilers of a small-tube, high-power type, and new lightweight Parsons turbines were fitted. Four 2pdr pompom mountings were installed on platforms around the funnel. Four guns from the 6in (152mm) secondary battery were removed, and the elevation of the main guns was raised to 30°, increasing the maximum range from 23,400yds (21,400m) to 29,000yds (26,500m).

Valiant and *Queen Elizabeth* were taken in hand for reconstruction along similar lines to *Warspite* in 1937–39 and 1939–41 respectively. They differed from the latter, however, in the layout of their machinery and in their armament. The 6in (152mm) gun battery was completely removed and replaced by ten of the new twin countersunk 4·5in (114mm) mountings. Four HACS directors of the latest design were installed in pairs forward and aft.

At the outbreak of war *Warspite*, *Malaya* and *Barham* were in the Mediterranean, while *Valiant* and *Queen Elizabeth* were still in dockyard hands. Towards the end of 1939 the Mediterranean-based ships returned to the Home Fleet, *Barham* being torpedoed by *U30* in the Clyde estuary in December. *Warspite* participated in the Norwegian campaign, and was present at the second battle of Narvik, in which she actively supported a British

Below: *Warspite* was the first ship of the class to undergo a complete reconstruction. The space and weight saved by fitting new boilers and turbines were utilised to provide a new anti-aircraft armament and extra horizontal protection. *Warspite* was later to serve with distinction in the Mediterranean.

Below: *Queen Elizabeth* in 1943, following refit and repair in the United States. Additional 20mm AA guns were carried from this time.

destroyer flotilla in the destruction of a number of German destroyers. In May she joined *Malaya* in the Eastern Mediterranean, the theatre in which she was to make her most important contribution to the course of the war. *Valiant* was also transferred to the Mediterranean Fleet in August 1940. *Barham*, meanwhile, had joined Force "H" at the other end of the Mediterranean, and was involved in operations against the French Fleet at Mers-el-Kebir and Dakar. She switched places with *Malaya* at the end of 1940. In March 1941 *Warspite*, *Valiant* and *Barham*, in company with the carrier *Formidable*, at last caught up with a substantial part of the Italian Fleet near Cape Matapan, and sank three heavy cruisers and two destroyers in a night battle.

The Mediterranean Fleet was reinforced by the newly modernised *Queen Elizabeth* in May 1941, but it was during this period that the fleet sustained its heaviest losses, with *Warspite*, *Valiant* and *Barham* being hit by bombs while supporting operations off Crete. Further serious losses were sustained at the end of 1941, when *Barham* was sunk off the Egyptian coast by three torpedoes from *U331*, and *Queen Elizabeth* and *Valiant* were badly damaged by Italian midget torpedoes.

Throughout 1941 *Malaya* served with Force "H", and although torpedoed in March was quickly repaired. She was employed as a convoy escort during the ▶

Above: *Valiant* in home waters in May 1943, shortly before her return to the Mediterranean for the final phase of the war against Italy. As modernised she could be distinguished from her sister *Queen Elizabeth* by the pole mainmast and the fitting of 20mm guns atop "A" and "Y" turrets.

relief of Malta in 1941–42. She returned to the UK in early 1943 and decommissioned later that year, recommissioning only for the Normandy invasion.

Warspite served with the Eastern Fleet from February 1942, but in 1943 returned to the Mediterranean for the landings in Sicily and at Salerno. At Salerno (September 1943) she was heavily damaged by a German glider bomb, and although repaired to enable her to support the Normandy landings she could by this time operate on only three shafts.

Valiant also served with the Eastern Fleet in 1942, returning for the landing operations in the Mediterranean in 1943. In January 1944 she joined the newly repaired *Queen Elizabeth* for a further spell in the Eastern Fleet, but was seriously damaged in a docking accident at Trincomalee and was never repaired. *Queen Elizabeth* continued to support British carrier operations in the Far East until the end of the war.

Right: *Queen Elizabeth* as she appeared following major repairs in the USA necessitated by serious damage sustained in an attack by Italian midget submarines in Alexandria in December 1941. Note the new twin 20mm AA mountings atop "A" turret.

Below: *Warspite* fires her forward 15in guns. During World War II she saw frequent employment in the fire support role, both in the Mediterranean and in the Channel. She continued operations off Normandy in spite of serious mine damage.

GREAT BRITAIN

Renown Class

Names: *Renown, Repulse.*
Laid down: 1915.
Completed: 1916.
Reconstructed: 1936–39 (*Renown* only).
Displacement: *Renown* 30,025 tons light, 36,080 tons full load; *Repulse* 32,130 tons light; 38,300 tons full load.
Dimensions: Length 794ft 2in (242m) oa; beam 101ft–102ft 4in (30·8–31·2m); draught 30ft 6in–31ft 6in (9·2–9·5m).
Propulsion: *Renown* Parsons geared steam turbines, 8 Admiralty boilers, 120,000shp, 4 shafts, 29·5kt; *Repulse* Brown-Curtis direct drive steam turbines, 42 Babcock & Wilcox boilers, 112,000shp, 4 shafts, 28·5kt.
Armour: Belt 9in–3in (230–75mm); deck 5in–2·5in (125–65mm) in *Renown*, 5·75in–3·5in (145–90mm) in *Repulse;* barbettes 7in–4in (180–100mm); turrets 11in–4·25in (280–110mm); conning tower 3in–2in (75–50mm).
Armament: 6 x 15in (381mm); 20 x 4·5in (114mm) DP in *Renown*, 12 x 4in (102mm), 6 x 4in AA in *Repulse;* 16/24 x 2pdr AA; 16 x 0·5in (12·7mm) AA; 8 x 21in (533mm) torpedo tubes.
Complement: 1,200–1,260.

56

Development: As completed in 1916, *Renown* and *Repulse* were identical in configuration, but whereas *Repulse* received only standard modifications during the interwar period, *Renown* underwent a total reconstruction which made her a much more effective fighting unit than her sister.

The two ships were originally designed as fast battlecruisers, with a heavy gun armament and exceptionally high speed, but with only light protection. Both were bulged and given additional vertical and horizontal armour in the 1920s. *Repulse* was refitted in 1933–36, when she received additional deck armour and an athwartships catapult and hangars (four aircraft) amidships. Her anti-aircraft armament was revised, but remained well below standard up to the time of her loss in late 1941. By 1939 she was overweight, and her maximum speed was little more than 28kt.

Renown was taken in hand in 1936 and was reconstructed on similar lines to the battleship *Warspite*. However, her modernisation, like that of *Valiant* and *Queen Elizabeth,* was more thorough, and she emerged in 1939 as the most successful of all British reconstructions. Eight Admiralty 3-drum boilers replaced the 42 Babcock & Wilcox boilers originally installed, and she was given new ▶

Below: *Repulse* fires her forward 15in guns while on exercises during the 1920s. In spite of their heavy armament, these ships were particularly lightly built and had relatively thin armour.

Right: *Repulse* as she appeared in April 1939. In a major refit in 1933–36 she received additional horizontal protection, an athwartships catapult and twin hangars amidships, and a modern anti-aircraft armament. She did not undergo a major reconstruction as did *Renown,* and at the outbreak of war she was rightly regarded as inferior to her sister in most respects. However, her high speed was still a useful asset to counter the German "pocket battleships" of the Deutschland class.

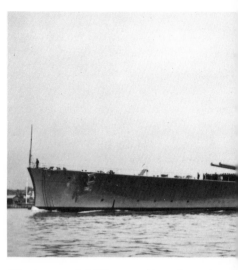

lightweight turbines. This modification saved 2,800 tons without loss of power, and the reduction from six to four boiler rooms created additional space for the magazines of the new 4·5in (114mm) anti-aircraft guns. Twenty of these were installed in twin countersunk turrets, controlled by four high-

Above: *Repulse* in December 1941, shortly before she was sunk in company with *Prince of Wales* by land-based bombers while attempting to oppose Japanese landings in Malaya.

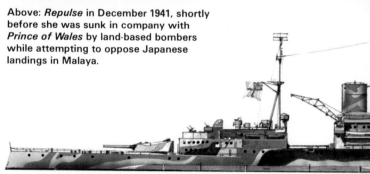

angle directors. The elevation of the main guns was increased from 20° to 30°, and additional armour was fitted on the decks and the barbettes. A catapult and hangars were installed amidships. The weight saved by the installation of new machinery and the removal of the former 4in (102mm) secondary armament was such that in spite of all these modifications *Renown* displaced 1,500 tons less at full load than she had before reconstruction.

At the outbreak of hostilities *Renown* and *Repulse*, together with *Hood*, formed the Battlecruiser Squadron of the Home Fleet. They spent much of the early part of the war chasing German surface raiders, which included *Deutschland* and *Graf Spee*. Both ships were at sea during the German occupation of Norway. In April 1940 *Renown* encountered *Scharnhorst* and *Gneisenau* in heavy weather, and inflicted serious damage on the latter before the German battlecruisers withdrew at high speed.

In 1940 *Renown* joined Force "H" at Gibraltar, and in 1941–42 was frequently employed as an escort for Malta convoys and relief operations. Both ships participated in the *Bismarck* chase, albeit without seeing action, but with tensions rising in the Pacific *Repulse* was prepared for service in the Far East. Together with the new battleship *Prince of Wales* she made up the ill-fated Force "Z", and she and her consort were sunk by land-based aircraft while attempting to strike at Japanese landings in Malaya. She received five torpedo hits and one bomb hit before capsizing. *Renown* also served in the Far East during 1944, but after returning to the UK in 1945 she was placed in reserve for the remainder of the war. Her light anti-aircraft armament had by this time increased to 28 x 2pdr (3 x 8, 1 x 4) and 64 x 20mm (20 x 2, 24 x 1).

Below: *Renown* in July 1942. The 4·5in dual-purpose mountings were in countersunk turrets.

Hood

Laid down: 1916.
Completed: 1920.
Displacement: 42,750 tons light; 48,650 tons full load.
Dimensions: Length 860ft 7in (262·8m) oa; beam 104ft 2in (31·8m); draught 32ft (9·7m).
Propulsion: Brown-Curtis geared steam turbines, 24 Yarrow boilers; 144,000shp; 4 shafts; 30kt.
Armour: Belt 12in–5in (305–125mm); deck 3in–1·5in (75–38mm); barbettes 12in–3in (305–75mm); turrets 15in–5in (380–125mm); conning tower 11in–3in (280–75mm).
Armament: 8 x 15in (381mm); 12 x 5·5in (140mm); 8 x 4in (102mm) DP; 24 x 2pdr AA; 16 x 0·5in (12·7mm) AA; 4 x 21in (533mm) torpedo tubes.
Complement: 1,397.

Below: HMS *Hood* shortly after completion. She was the last battlecruiser to be completed by any navy, the type being superseded in the 1930s by the "fast battleship".

Above: *Hood* as she appeared at completion; the photograph was probably taken during her trials. She was still the largest and fastest capital ship in the world when war broke out in 1939.

Below: Following a refit in 1931-32 *Hood* carried an experimental aircraft installation comprising a telescoping catapult on the quarterdeck. It was removed before World War II.

Development: The original design for the battlecruiser *Hood* dates from before Jutland. She and her three projected sisters were intended to counter the German battlecruisers of the Mackensen class, which were rumoured to have 15in (381mm) guns. Essentially a "Fisher design", *Hood* was to have a heavy gun armament and high speed, but relatively light protection. After Jutland, however, the plans were hurriedly redrawn and armour thicknesses increased by 50 per cent, resulting in a displacement 5,000 tons greater than in the original design and the loss of about 2kt of speed. The three sisterships were cancelled in 1917, when it was learnt that work on the new German battlecruisers had ceased, but *Hood* was duly completed in 1920. She remained the world's largest and fastest capital ship for many years, and enjoyed a high reputation in the British fleet.

Hood, however, suffered on the one hand from being designed too early to incorporate the full lessons of Jutland, and on the other from being completed too late to justify major reconstruction such as was given to battleships of the Queen Elizabeth class and to the battlecruiser *Renown* during the interwar period. She had an elaborate system of internal protection, designed to explode large-calibre shells before they reached vital equipment deep inside the ship, but the horizontal plating was of inadequate thickness to cope with plunging shells fired at the longer ranges of engagement which were by then becoming accepted. The vertical protection was better, with a sloped main armour belt 12in (305mm) thick and an integral torpedo bulge, which utilised hollow steel tubes 8ft (2·4m) long and 1in (25cm) in diameter in an outer destruction space, spare fuel oil in the inner destruction space, plus a series of longitudinal bulkheads. ▶

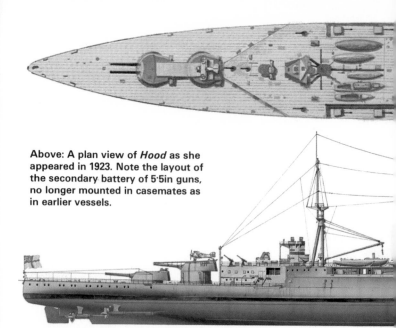

Above: A plan view of *Hood* as she appeared in 1923. Note the layout of the secondary battery of 5·5in guns, no longer mounted in casemates as in earlier vessels.

The secondary battery of 5·5in (140mm) guns was mounted in open shields along the upper deck and at the forward end of the shelter deck. It was therefore relatively unprotected but could be worked in a seaway, which constituted an improvement on the arrangements in earlier vessels.

In December 1938 it was proposed that *Hood* undergo a reconstruction

Above: *Hood* as she would have appeared following the reconstruction proposed in December 1938 (for details see text).

Below: The Battlecruiser Squadron at Scapa Flow, probably in late 1939. *Hood* is centre picture, *Renown* on the left.

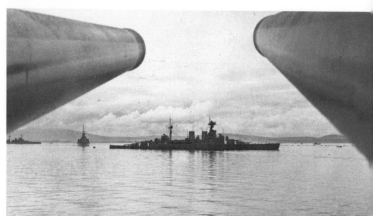

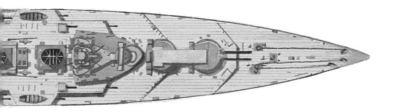

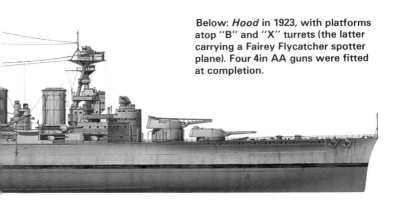

Below: *Hood* in 1923, with platforms atop "B" and "X" turrets (the latter carrying a Fairey Flycatcher spotter plane). Four 4in AA guns were fitted at completion.

similar to that of *Renown,* but with sixteen 5·25in (133mm) guns as in the King George V class. The replacement of the existing machinery was considered especially urgent. The reconstruction was, however, cancelled with the outbreak of war, and the ship remained largely unmodified.

In September 1939 *Hood* was flagship of the Battlecruiser Squadron, and served with the Home Fleet until March 1940. She then underwent a two-month refit in which all the 5·5in (140mm) guns were removed, and three additional twin 4in (102mm) mountings were fitted. She was also given five of the new (but ineffectual) UP mountings.

Hood served with Force "H" from June 1940, and was Vice-Admiral Somerville's flagship when he called on the French Fleet at Mers-el-Kebir to surrender. She returned to Rosyth in September, and served with the Home Fleet until May 1941, when she and the new battleship *Prince of Wales* were given the task of intercepting *Bismarck* and *Prinz Eugen* in the Denmark Strait. She was hit first by the cruiser, and then by *Bismarck's* fifth salvo, which is thought to have penetrated the after magazines. She and all but three of her crew were lost in the resulting explosion.

Right: The fateful encounter involving *Hood* and the new battleship *Prince of Wales,* and the German *Bismarck.* Vice-Admiral Holland, well aware of the inadequacies of *Hood's* horizontal protection, endeavoured to meet the German ships head on, but instead found himself on their beam.

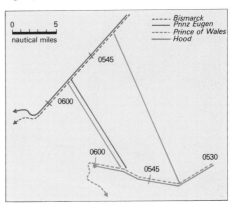

Nelson Class

Names: *Nelson, Rodney.*
Laid down: 1922.
Completed: 1927.
Displacement: 36,000–37,000 tons standard; 43,150–44,050 tons full load.
Dimensions: Length 710ft (216·4m) oa; beam 106ft (32·3m); draught 34ft (10·2m).
Propulsion: Brown-Curtis geared steam turbines, 8 Admiralty boilers; 45,000shp; 2 shafts; 23kt.
Armour: Belt 14in–13in (355–330mm); deck 6·25in–3·25in (160–80mm); barbettes 15in–12in (380–305mm); turrets 16in–7·25in (405–185mm); conning tower 14in–6·5in (355–165mm).
Armament: 9 x 16in (406mm); 12 x 6in (152mm); 6 x 4·7in (120mm) AA; 16/24 x 2pdr AA; 8 x 0·5in (12·7mm) AA; 2 x 24·5in (622mm) torpedo tubes.
Complement: 1,314.

Development: The two battleships of the Nelson class have their origins in a series of new designs projected at the time of the Washington Conference. According to the terms of the agreement, Britain was allowed to complete two new battleships, but these were to be subjected to the limitation on displacement (35,000 tons standard) and armament (16in, 406mm, maximum) established by the Treaty. The design was therefore a scaled-down version of the "G3" battlecruiser, with nine 16in (406mm) guns in triple turrets and armour sufficient to withstand 16in (406mm) shells, but with a substantial reduction in speed. The battlecruisers were to have had 160,000shp for 31–32kt; in the Nelson class this figure was reduced to only 45,000shp for 23kt.

Nelson and *Rodney* introduced a number of novel features to battleship construction. Their three triple turrets were concentrated forward of the bridge in order to shorten the length of the citadel. Furthermore, the "all or nothing" system of protection pioneered by the US Navy was adopted, so that the maximum thickness of armour could be concentrated on the side belt and on the single heavy armoured deck which rested on its top edge.

Nelson was the first battleship in the world to have her secondary battery mounted in turrets. This enabled the guns to be worked in all weather conditions, but the light armour plating (1in, 25mm) on the turrets and their close grouping attracted some criticism. Other unusual features were the new "tower" bridge structure, which served as a model for all later British capital ships, and the location of the turbines forward of the boiler rooms, to enable the single funnel to be placed well clear of the bridge.

Not all the innovative features were successful. The triple turrets gave ▶

Above: *Nelson* fires her big guns. The photograph probably dates from 1942–43, when she supported the Allied landings in North Africa, Sicily and Italy by bombarding enemy positions near the beach-head.

Above: *Nelson* fires a broadside. The all-forward main armament arrangement was unique for a three-turret ship but was also favoured by the French in the battleships built in the 1930s.

Below: *Rodney* as she appeared in 1942. Additional 2pdr pompoms and numerous single 20mm Oerlikons had been fitted by this time.

trouble, and even after modification the rate of fire per gun was only one shell every 45 seconds. Blast damage when the guns were fired was considerable, and restrictions had to be placed on the training arcs of "C" turret. The propulsion machinery, which had been selected because of its low weight, was subject to frequent breakdowns.

At the outbreak of war *Nelson* and *Rodney* constituted the backbone of the British Home Fleet. *Nelson* received severe mine damage in December 1939, and *Rodney* was hit by a 1,100lb (500kg) bomb while operating off Norway in

Below: *Nelson* (foreground) and her sister *Rodney* at Gibraltar in July 1943, when they undertook fire support operations off Sicily. As the new battleships of the King George V class were commissioned, the Nelsons were deployed from the Home Fleet to the western Mediterranean, where they performed valuable service.

April 1940. As the new battleships of the King George V class began to enter service they were relegated to Atlantic convoy escort duties, during which period *Rodney* participated in the final destruction of the *Bismarck*. *Nelson* joined Force "H" in June, but was struck by an airborne torpedo off Sardinia in September while covering a Malta convoy; she was relieved by *Rodney* while under repair. In 1943 both ships provided fire support at Sicily and Salerno. By this time the close-range AA armament had been substantially increased: *Rodney* had 44 x 2pdr (5 x 8, 1 x 4) and 66 x 20mm (5 x 2, 56 x 1), and *Nelson* 48 x 2pdr (6 x 8) and 61 x 20mm (61 x 1). In 1944 the ships were deployed in support of the Normandy landings. *Nelson* struck a mine in June, and after repairs in the USA, during which four quadruple 40mm mountings were fitted, served with the Eastern Fleet until the end of the war. *Rodney*, which was by this time in poor mechanical condition, was placed in reserve in December 1944. Both ships were broken up soon after the war.

King George V Class

Names: *King George V, Prince of Wales, Duke of York, Anson, Howe.*
Laid down: 1937.
Completed: 1940–42.
Displacement: 36,750 tons standard; 42,080 tons full load.
Dimensions: length 745ft (227·1m) oa; beam 103ft (31·4m); draught 32ft
6in (9·9m).
Propulsion: Parsons geared steam turbines, 8 Admiralty boilers;
110,000shp; 4 shafts; 28kt.
Armour: Belt 15in–4·5in (380–115mm); deck 6in–5in (150–125mm);
barbettes 13in–11in (330–280mm); turrets 12·75in–5·9in (325–150mm);
conning tower 4·5in–2in (115–50mm).
Armament: 10 x 14in (356mm); 16 x 5·25in (133mm) DP; 32/48 x 2pdr AA;
3/4 UP mountings in *King George V, Prince of Wales.*
Complement: 1,422.

Development: The design of the battleships of the King George V class was
heavily constrained from the outset by political considerations. In the London
Treaty of 1930 Britain, the USA and Japan had agreed to a five-year
moratorium on new construction. This meant that no new British battleships
could be laid down before January 1937, even though the French and Italians
(who refused to sign the London Treaty) and the Germans (who had made a
separate agreement with Britain) had already begun the construction of fast,
powerful battleships of their own. Moreover, the British were still hoping to
obtain agreement at the next conference, due to take place in 1936, on a 14in
(356mm) maximum gun calibre for new construction. In the event both the
USA and Japan refused to accept this limitation, and subsequently laid down
ships with 16in (406mm) and 18in (460mm) guns. Britain, however, could not
afford to wait for the results of the negotiations because of the lead already
established by her European rivals. If the new battleships were to be begun in

**Above: A plan view of
Prince of Wales as she
appeared in late 1941. The
UP mountings have been
replaced by 20mm guns.**

Above: A battleship of the King George V class, probably *Duke of York,* in heavy weather. These ships bore the brunt of the war at sea in the northern theatre, protecting the Murmansk convoys against the German battleships based in northern Norway; *Duke of York* herself accounted for the German battlecruiser *Scharnhorst.*

January 1937, their guns would have to be ordered prior to this date in order to ensure early completion. The British therefore opted for the 14in (356mm) gun in anticipation of an agreement.

The design process had begun as early as 1934, the year in which the Italian Littorios were laid down. The emphasis was on a heavy main armament — comprising either 9 x 16in (406mm), 9 x 15in (381mm) or 12 x 14in (356mm) guns — and protection against 16in (406mm) shells. A speed of only 23kt was initially favoured, as this was deemed adequate for ships that would form a ▶

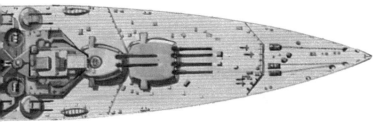

Below: *Prince of Wales* as she appeared on arrival at Singapore in December 1941. The camouflage is a First Admiralty Disruptive type, and the aircraft is a Supermarine Walrus I.

homogeneous battle-line with the older British ships, some of which were being reconstructed. However, concern about the high speed of the new Italian and German capital ships led to a revision of the design to give a speed of 27–28kt, and since displacement was fixed at the Treaty maximum of 35,000 tons standard, the additional horsepower had to be bought by a reduction in the number of 14in (356mm) guns from twelve to ten; this in turn meant that a new twin turret had to be designed, which was to cause further delays.

When the Treaty moratorium finally expired, the entire class of five ships was laid down in the space of six months, and the first ship was completed in less than four years.

The 14in (356mm) Mk VII gun fired a heavyweight shell (1,590lb, 720kg) at a modest velocity, and at the maximum 40° elevation it had a range of 36,000yds (32,900m). The design of the mountings was based on that of the World War I 15in (381mm) mounting, except that the magazines were located below the shell rooms. This complicated the hoist arrangements, but a rate of fire of two rounds per minute was still achieved. The complexity of the mounting was also increased by the desire to make it as flash-tight as possible. Frequent breakdowns in the guns and mountings occurred when the early ships were first completed, notably aboard the brand new *Prince of Wales* during the *Bismarck* engagement, when both "A" and "Y" turrets jammed. However, these initial problems had been ironed out by 1942, and the gun subsequently proved very effective in service.

The King George V class were unique among the newly built European capital ships in mounting a dual-purpose secondary armament, which comprised eight of the new twin 5·25in (133mm) mountings. To enable them to continue firing even after the failure of the ship's own generators, the turrets were self-contained with their own power supply. Although the guns elevated to 70°, high-angle engagements were not up to expectations because of the low rate of fire (10–12rpm designed, but in practice only 7–8rpm) and of training (only 10–11° per second).

Originally the ships were to have carried only four 2pdr pompom mountings. This figure rose to six by the end of 1939, but a shortage of mountings led to the installation of UP mountings on the first two ships. These were later replaced by 20mm guns, and by 1945 all surviving ships carried eight octuple and six quadruple pompoms (not in *King George V*), 8–26 x 40mm Bofors, and 8–65 x 20mm. ▶

Left: *King George V* entering Chesapeake Bay in 1941 shortly before her action against *Bismarck*. In the original design there were to have been three quadruple turrets, but one of these was altered to a twin mounting to provide enhanced protection.

Below: *Anson* fires off a salvo from "A" turret during trials. The camouflage is an Admiralty Intermediate Disruptive Type.

Protection was on the same "all or nothing" scheme as in *Nelson*, but was revised as a result of testing in the 1920s and 1930s. There was a greater armoured reserve of buoyancy, improved protection against diving shells, a reduction in the unarmoured structure above the citadel, and some protection for the soft ends of the ship. The depth of the main belt was a full 24ft (7·5m) — a figure which compared favourably with all foreign construction. There was a single thick armoured deck, and the underwater protection system was designed to withstand a 1,000lb (450kg) torpedo warhead.

The layout of the machinery was on the same "unit" system employed in contemporary British cruisers, with two independent groups of turbines and boilers which could be cross-connected in the event of action damage.

When completed all ships were initially deployed with the Home Fleet. *Anson* and *Howe* did not enter service until late 1942 because of a 3–6 month suspension of their construction in May 1940 to free shipyard resources for the building of much-needed escorts. *Prince of Wales* was rushed into action against the *Bismarck* while she still had shipyard contractors aboard, but still

Below: *Howe* in 1942. On completion she was quickly pressed into service in support of the Arctic convoys. She was later to deploy to the Mediterranean and to the Pacific.

managed to secure two hits before she was forced to break off the engagement. *King George V,* at that time the flagship of the C-in-C Home Fleet, played a leading role in the final destruction of the German battleship.

Following service with Force "H" in mid-1941, *Prince of Wales* became the flagship of the ill-fated British squadron sent to the Far East. She subsequently became the first modern battleship to be sunk by air attack. She was hit by five torpedoes, the first of which caused severe flooding aft and put five of the eight generators out of action; this led to some revision of arrangements in the later *Vanguard.*

The year 1942 saw the introduction of the Arctic convoys, and each successive convoy was given a distant escort which comprised at least one ship of the King George V class to counter the threat posed by *Tirpitz, Scharnhorst* and the remaining two German pocket battleships. In December 1943, while providing support for a convoy to Murmansk, *Duke of York* engaged and sank *Scharnhorst.* Her performance in this action was such that the German battlecruiser was heavily hit before she could reply effectively. With *Tirpitz* crippled by midget submarines and bombing attacks, *King George V* and her sisters were transferred to the Far East, where they served as flagships, carrier escorts and fire support ships in the newly created British Pacific Fleet. All four ships were decommissioned between 1946 and 1950.

Vanguard

Laid down: 1941.
Completed: 1946.
Displacement: 44,500 tons standard; 51,420 tons full load.
Dimensions: Length 814ft 4in (248·2m) oa; beam 108ft (32·9m); draught 34ft 10in (10·6m).
Propulsion: Parsons geared steam turbines, 8 Admiralty boilers; 130,000shp; 4 shafts; 30kt.
Armour: Belt 14in–4·5in (355–115mm); deck 6in–5in (150–125mm); barbettes 13in–11in (330–280mm); turrets 13in–7in (330–180mm); conning tower 3in–2·5in (75–65mm).
Armament: 8 x 15in (381mm); 16 x 5·25in (133mm) DP; 73 x 40mm AA.
Complement: 1,893.

Development: When the British failed to secure agreement on a 14in (356mm) maximum gun calibre at the 1936 conference, there was some concern that the battle fleet would be outgunned by contemporary foreign battleships, and a modification of the King George V class armed with nine 16in (406mm) guns was approved. Two of the four ships projected, *Lion* and *Temeraire,* were laid down in mid-1939, but construction was suspended just after the outbreak of war in order to release shipyard labour for more urgent work, and they were subsequently cancelled.

A major factor in the cancellation of the Lion class was the time required to produce the 16in (406mm) gun mountings. However, the Royal Navy had available four twin 15in (381mm) mountings previously removed from the light ▶

Above: *Vanguard* was designed to incorporate a number of lessons learned as a result of wartime experience with the King George V class; in particular, the bow was given increased sheer and flare in order to improve sea-keeping. The modification proved successful, and *Vanguard* was an excellent seaboat.

Below: *Vanguard* in 1947, the year in which she took members of the British royal family on a tour of South Africa. She was subsequently employed as a training ship, and after a period in reserve was finally sold to the breakers in 1960, without ever having fired her guns in anger. *Vanguard* was the Royal Navy's last battleship.

battlecruisers *Courageous* and *Glorious* on their conversion to aircraft carriers. A design for a "fully armoured battlecruiser" projected as a counter to the Japanese heavy cruisers had been considered in early 1939, and this became the basis of Britain's last battleship, *Vanguard,* which was finally laid down in 1941.

In order to avoid delays the machinery of the Lion class was adopted. However, as a result of experience with the loss of the *Prince of Wales,* four (not two) of the eight generators were diesel-driven, to avoid the loss of power which would otherwise result from failure of the ship's boilers.

Protection was generally similar to that of the King George V class, although some modifications were again made in the light of war experience. There was more extensive splinter protection, and the height of the longitudinal bulkheads was raised to prevent the rapid flooding which occurred when *Prince of Wales* was struck aft by a Japanese airborne torpedo. More emphasis was placed on endurance, presumably with operations in the Far East in mind. Fuel capacity was substantially increased, and sea-keeping was improved by increasing freeboard forward. A full range of the latest radar equipment was installed for surveillance and fire control.

The 15in (381mm) turrets were modified for installation aboard *Vanguard.* Elevation was increased to 30°, thicker plating was fitted, the 15ft (4·6m)

Above: *Vanguard* fires a salvo from her 15in guns. The adoption of spare gun mountings from the former battlecruisers *Courageous* and *Glorious* speeded the construction of the ship.

Above: *Vanguard* in August 1946. The dual-purpose armament of 5·25in guns and the homogeneous battery of multiple 40mm mountings are particularly evident in this view. A new sextuple mounting (Mk VI) was adopted to replace the 2pdr pompom.

rangefinders were replaced by 30ft (9·2m) models, and remote power control for training was provided. The secondary 5·25in (133mm) turrets, unlike those aboard the King George V class, also had remote power control, both for training and for elevation.

The anti-aircraft armament was substantially increased in the light of war experience. Originally it was intended to fit ten 2pdr pompoms, which could be accommodated only by omitting the aircraft handling arrangements. In the event, however, the Mk VI pompom was replaced by a new sextuple 40mm Bofors mounting (Mk VI), and the 20mm mountings were discarded in favour of single power-operated 40mm Bofors (Mk VII), giving *Vanguard* a homogeneous light AA battery. High-angle control was provided by four US Mk 37 directors with Type 275 radar.

Vanguard may not have been the most powerful battleship produced in World War II, but she was arguably the most well-balanced. Fast, exceptionally seaworthy and well-protected, she would undoubtedly have proved successful had she been completed in time for war service. In the event, she was deployed only on peacetime cruises in the postwar period, and was placed in reserve in the mid-1950s.

Below: *Vanguard* in 1946; note the sheer forward and the transom stern. A full outfit of search and FC radars is carried.

Conte di Cavour Class

Names: *Conte di Cavour, Giulio Cesare.*
Laid down: 1910.
Completed: 1914–15.
Reconstructed: 1933–37.
Displacement: 26,140 tons standard; 29,030 tons full load.
Dimensions: Length 611ft 9in (186·4m) oa; beam 91ft 10in (28m); draught 34ft 1in (10·4m).
Propulsion: Belluzzo geared steam turbines, 8 Yarrow boilers; 93,000shp; 2 shafts; 28kt.
Armour: Belt 10in–5in (250–130mm); decks 1·6in + 1·6in + 4in–3·2in (40mm + 40mm + 100–80mm); barbettes 11·4in–11in (290–280mm); turrets 11in–9in (280–230mm); conning tower 10·4in–4in (260–100mm).
Armament: 10 x 12·6in (320mm); 12 x 4·7in (120mm); 8 x 3·9in (100mm) AA; 12 x 37mm AA; 12 x 13·2mm AA.
Complement: 1,236.

Development: Completed in 1914–15 as conventional dreadnought battleships, with a main armament of 13 x 12in (305mm) guns and a maximum speed of 21–22kt, *Cavour* and *Cesare* were completely rebuilt during the mid-1930s. The original machinery, which comprised a mixture of oil- and coal-fired

Below: *Cavour* **in the late 1930s, after her reconstruction. The four surviving Italian dreadnoughts underwent the most extensive reconstruction of all the world's older battleships,** *Cavour's* **being modelled on that of contemporary Italian cruisers. The centre turret was removed and the other guns were bored out.**

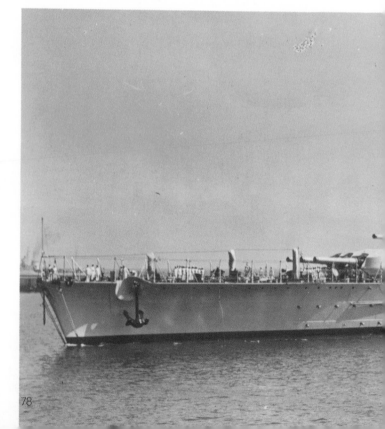

Above: *Conte di Cavour* **in 1917. As originally completed these ships had a fifth turret between tall twin funnels.**

boilers and Parsons turbines, was replaced by lightweight turbines of Italian manufacture and modern oil-fired boilers, and the number of shafts was reduced from four to two. The weight thus saved was used to enhance the horizontal protection which, nevertheless, remained inadequate by the standards of new and modernised foreign capital ships. A Pugliese underwater protection system (see Littorio class) was incorporated, but this was rendered less effective than it might have been by the relatively narrow beam of the ships. The bows and stern were lengthened and remodelled to improve the length-to-beam ratio, and both ships exceeded their designed (conversion) speed of 26kt by about 2kt on trials. ▶

A novel solution was adopted for the main battery. The midships triple 12in mounting was removed to allow for the fitting of modern secondary and anti-aircraft batteries, and the remaining ten guns were bored out and relined to give a 12·6in (320mm) calibre. The mountings were also modified to give a maximum elevation of 27°, for a maximum range of 31,300yds (28,600m). The firepower of these ships as converted therefore closely matched that of the French *Dunkerque* and *Strasbourg,* and they outranged the older battleships of the Royal Navy which faced them in the Mediterranean by a substantial margin.

The secondary battery of 12 x 4·7in (120mm) was on the light side to counter destroyer attacks, but was disposed in modern twin turrets. The upperworks were completely rebuilt on the lines of the latest Italian light cruisers of the "Condottieri" type, with a small turret bridge structure carrying the main fire control directors, two small funnels, and a tall tripod mainmast.

Above: *Cesare* in 1938, showing the forward main gun turrets and the new turret bridge structure. The fire control director atop the bridge is for the main battery of 12·6in guns, and the smaller director is for the secondary 4·7in battery.

Below: *Cesare* in 1940, displaying the battle damage sustained during the action off Calabria, when she was hit amidships by a 15in shell from the British battleship *Warspite*. Twin 37mm AA mountings can be seen on either side of the damaged funnel.

Above: *Cavour* **underway in the Mediterranean. During reconstruction the bow was completely remodelled and given greater flare for improved sea-keeping. The stern was also lengthened, and with new machinery speed rose from 21·5kt before refit to 27-28kt.**

Cesare and *Cavour* were the only Italian battleships in full commission when that country entered the war in May 1940. In July they encountered the battleships of the British Mediterranean Fleet off Calabria, but an early hit on *Cesare* at very long range by *Warspite* caused the Italians to break off the action. Thereafter they and the other Italian battleships were employed against British convoys to Malta and against Force "H" in the Western Mediterranean, but their forays were always tempered by extreme caution and a reluctance to get involved in action with heavy units. In the attack on Taranto in November 1940 by aircraft from the carrier *Illustrious, Cavour* was sunk in shallow water by a single torpedo, and although she was raised in July 1941 and towed to Trieste for repairs she never saw service again. In January 1941 *Cesare* received slight damage from three near-misses when the fleet was bombed at Naples. In December 1941 and January 1942 she was employed as a distant escort for military convoys to North Africa, after which she was decommissioned. In 1949 she was ceded to the Soviet Union, and as the *Novorossiysk* she served as a training ship. She sank in October 1955 in Sevastopol Roads, probably as a result of striking a mine.

Caio Duilio Class

Names: *Caio Duilio, Andrea Doria.*
Laid down: 1912.
Completed: 1915–16.
Reconstructed: 1937–40.
Displacement: 26,430/25,920 tons standard; 29,390/28,880 tons full load.
Dimensions: Length 613ft 3in (186·9m) oa; beam 91ft 10in (28m); draught 29ft 2in (8·9m).
Propulsion: Belluzzo geared steam turbines, 8 Yarrow boilers; 87,000shp; 2 shafts; 27kt.
Armour: Belt 10in–5in (250–130mm); decks 1·25in + 1·6in + 4in–3·2in (32mm + 40mm + 100–80mm); barbettes 11·4in–11in (290–280mm); turrets 11in–9in (280–230mm); conning tower 10·4in–4in (260–100mm).
Armament: 10 x 12·6in (320mm); 12 x 5·3in (135mm); 10 x 3·5in (90mm) AA; 15 x 37mm AA; 16 x 20mm AA.
Complement: 1,485.

Development: The two former 12in (305mm) gun dreadnoughts of the Caio Duilio class were completely rebuilt during the late 1930s on the lines of their near-sisters of the Cavour class. They were taken in hand when the reconstructions of *Cavour* and *Cesare* were nearing completion, and a number of additional modifications were made, many of which were also features of the new battleships of the Littorio class.

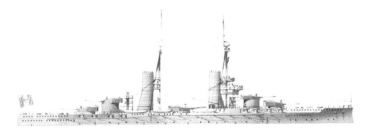

Above: *Andrea Doria* as completed in 1916. The Duilios differed from the Cavours in the funnel/mast layout; they also had a 6in secondary battery, and the centre turret was lower.

The most important difference between the Cavour and Duilio classes as modernised was the composition and layout of the secondary and anti-aircraft batteries. *Cavour* had her 4·7in (120mm) secondary guns disposed in twin turrets along the ship's sides, with twin 3·9in (100mm) AA mountings forward and aft of the secondary guns. In *Duilio* and *Doria,* however, the calibre of the secondary battery was raised to 5·3in (135mm), and the guns were mounted in superimposed triple turrets abreast the bridge structure. The raising of the ▶

Below: *Duilio* after reconstruction. Although rebuilt on essentially the same lines as the Cavours, she and her sister *Andrea Doria* owed more to the Littorios in their general appearance.

Above: *Andrea Doria* in company with *Cesare* in December 1941, when they provided long-distance cover for a North African convoy.

calibre to 5·3in (135mm) made considerable sense, as although the 4·7in (120mm) gun was the standard main armament of Italian destroyers, their French counterparts were armed with guns of 5·1in (130mm) calibre, and the large, fast *contre-torpilleurs* mounted guns of 5·5in (138·6mm) calibre. More

Above: *Duilio* at anchor during 1941–42. She and the other older battleships were not used offensively after 1940, instead supporting military convoys to North Africa from late 1941 until March 1942.

importantly, *Duilio* and *Doria* were given a battery of ten of the latest 3·5in (90mm) AA guns. As in the new battleships of the Littorio class, these were disposed in single mountings abreast the funnels.

The upperworks were also redesigned on the lines of the Littorios. The turret bridge structure was taller than that of the Cavours, with the fire control directors superimposed one above the other atop the navigation bridge. In place of the heavy tripod mainmast of *Cavour* there was a short, stubby pole mast to which were attached the twin booms for handling the ships' boats.

Both ships recommissioned only after Italy had entered World War II, *Duilio* in June 1940 and *Doria* not until October of that year. *Duilio* took part in an unsuccessful action by the Italian fleet against a British Mediterranean convoy in September 1940, and in November was struck by a torpedo during the attack on Taranto by British carrier aircraft. Unlike *Cavour,* however, she stayed afloat and was subsequently repaired. In December 1941 and January 1942 both ships were employed as escorts for military convoys to North Africa, and in February 1942 they took part in an unsuccessful action against a British convoy to Malta. In March 1942 they were withdrawn from active service. They surrendered with the rest of the Italian fleet in September 1943, and when handed back in June 1944 were employed as training ships. Both were scrapped during the 1950s.

Below: *Andrea Doria* as she appeared in late 1941. Note the triple 5·3in mountings abreast the bridge and the distinctive single 3·5in AA mountings amidships.

ITALY
Littorio Class

Names: *Littorio, Vittorio Veneto, Impero, Roma.*
Laid down: 1934–38.
Completed: 1940–42.
Displacement: 41,170–41,650 tons standard; 45,030–45,485 tons full load.
Dimensions: Length 780ft (237·8m) oa except *Roma, Impero* 789ft 6in
(240·7m); beam 107ft 5in (32·9m); draught 34ft 6in (10·5m).
Propulsion: Belluzzo geared steam turbines, 8 Yarrow boilers; 128,200shp;
4 shafts; 30kt.
Armour: Belt 2·75in + 11in–2·4in (70mm + 280–60mm); decks 1·4in +
6in–4in (35mm + 150–100mm); barbettes 14in–11in (350–280mm); turrets
14in–8in (350–200mm); conning tower 10in–2·4in (250–60mm).
Armament: 9 x 15in (381mm); 12 x 6in (152mm); 12 x 3·5in (90mm) AA; 20
x 37mm AA; 16/28 x 20mm AA.
Complement: 1,830–1,885.

Development: The Italians, refusing to be bound by the London Treaty
moratorium on new capital ship construction, were the first to lay down battleships of the maximum displacement allowed under the Washington Treaty.
Faced with a choice between three vessels of 23,000 tons each and two vessels
of 35,000 tons to use up their 70,000 tons of permitted battleship tonnage, they
opted for the latter course in order to counteract the construction of the
French *Dunkerque* and *Strasbourg*. A further two ships were laid down in the
late 1930s.

The 16in (406mm) gun was rejected because Italian industry was incapable
of producing the steel forgings, and a new 15in (381mm) model, with a
maximum range of 46,800–48,800yds (42,800–44,640m), was adopted. The
15in (381mm) guns were mounted in three triple turrets, the after turret being
raised above the forecastle deck in order to protect the spotter/reconnaissance
aircraft carried on the stern catapult from blast.

Separate secondary and anti-aircraft batteries were maintained. The twelve
6in (152mm) guns were mounted in triple turrets at the four "corners" of the

Above: *Vittorio Veneto* following sea trials, after which the bow section was given increased flare to improve sea-keeping.

ship. These turrets were particularly heavily armoured in comparison with those of contemporary foreign battleships; the faces were 11in (280mm) thick and the roofs 5in (130mm). A powerful anti-aircraft battery was fitted, comprising twelve 3·5in (90mm) guns in single mountings, plus large numbers of 37mm and 20mm guns.

The protection system was similar in some respects to that of American battleships, with a lightly armoured upper deck to burst bombs and AP shells before they reached the main armoured deck covering the ship's vitals. The side belt, which was sloped internally at 11°, was neither as thick nor as deep as the side belts of foreign battleships, but the total weight of armour accounted for 14,070 tons, some 37 per cent of the light displacement. ▶

Below: *Roma* as completed in mid-1942. She differed from the earlier two ships in having a lengthened bow with greater sheer. Note the high position of "X" turret, adopted in order to keep the quarterdeck free from blast for the three floatplanes.

The underwater system was designed by the Italian engineer Pugliese, and comprised a hollow longitudinal cylinder with a diameter of about 12ft (3·75m) floating in fuel oil and water within a bulged compartment. In theory a torpedo would expend its energy deforming the cylinder, but in practice the system was not as effective as it should have been because of poor structural connections.

Although the protection proved deficient in some respects, the Littorios were faster than most of their contemporaries. Speeds in excess of 31kt were obtained on trials by the first two ships, *Vittorio Veneto* and *Littorio*. However, some problems were experienced initially with the shape of the bows, which caused severe vibration forward and threw up a heavy spray; they were therefore lengthened by 6ft (1·8m). The second pair, *Roma* and *Impero*, were modified on the slipway and their bows were given a more prominent sheer.

Vittorio Veneto and *Littorio* had only just commissioned when Italy entered World War II, and were not ready for service until late August 1940. During the autumn they sortied against British naval forces in the Mediterranean on several occasions, but failed to press home their undoubted advantage in firepower. In the aerial attack on Taranto in November 1940 *Littorio* was seriously damaged by three torpedoes, and her bows settled on the bottom in shallow water; repairs took until August 1941. In March 1941 *Vittorio Veneto*, with the Italian C-in-C on board, sortied with two divisions of heavy cruisers and one of light cruisers to intercept British convoys bound for Greece. A British cruiser division was encountered, and an inconclusive skirmish ensued. However, the British Mediterranean Fleet, comprising the battleships *Warspite*, *Barham* and *Valiant*, accompanied by the carrier *Formidable*, was in support some 70nm (130km) away, and when the Italian battleship was attacked by aircraft from *Formidable* she broke off the action and a stern chase ensued. A second attack by aircraft from *Formidable* resulted in a torpedo striking *Veneto* just above the port outer shaft, causing power loss and flooding. Good damage control saved the ship, but a further torpedo hit on the cruiser *Pola* resulted in the loss of three of Italy's most powerful heavy cruisers in a night battle off Cape Matapan.

By September 1941 *Vittorio Veneto* and *Littorio* were again in commission,

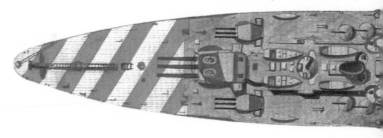

Above: Plan view of *Vittorio Veneto* with recognition stripes. Note the separate secondary and heavy AA batteries.

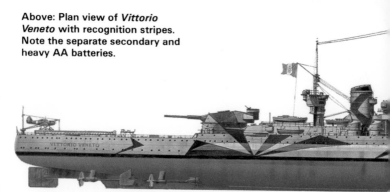

Above: *Vittorio Veneto* at Taranto in 1941-42. She provided distant cover for convoys to North Africa during this period.

and were employed against Malta convoys and also as distant escorts for Italian convoys to North Africa. During one of the latter operations *Veneto* was struck by a torpedo from the submarine *Urge* and was under repair until the spring of 1942. In June *Littorio* and *Vittorio Veneto* undertook what was to prove their final sortie against the Malta convoys. *Littorio* was struck by an airborne torpedo and a bomb, and was under repair until the following year.

Roma commissioned only in June 1942, and saw no active service. When the Italian fleet sailed for Malta to surrender she was struck by two German glider bombs, one of which penetrated right to the ship's bottom and the other to the forward magazines, which exploded. She sank with heavy loss of life. *Littorio*, which had by then been renamed *Italia*, was also hit by a glider bomb, but she and *Veneto* survived and were later scrapped.

Impero, the fourth ship of the class, was moved from Genoa to Brindisi at the outbreak of war because of fears of French attacks. Although she had been launched ten months ahead of *Roma*, work had to be suspended because of a shortage of steel, and she was never completed.

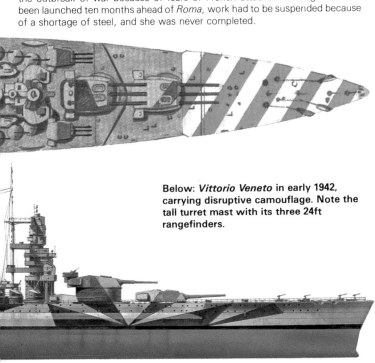

Below: *Vittorio Veneto* in early 1942, carrying disruptive camouflage. Note the tall turret mast with its three 24ft rangefinders.

Kongo Class

Names: *Kongo, Hiei, Haruna, Kirishima.*
Laid down: 1911–12.
Completed: 1913–15.
Reconstructed: 1927–30, 1933–40.
Displacement: 31,720–32,350 tons standard; 36,320 tons full load.
Dimensions: Length 728ft 7in (222·1m) oa; beam 95ft 3in (29m); draught 32ft (9·7m).
Propulsion: Kanpon geared steam turbines, 8/11 Kanpon boilers; 136,000shp; 4 shafts; 30kt.
Armour: Belt 8in–3in (205–75mm); deck 4·7in–2in (120–50mm); barbettes 10in (255mm) max; turrets 9in (230mm) max; conning tower 10in–6in (255–155mm).
Armament: 8 x 14in (356mm); 14 x 6in (152mm); 8 x 5in (127mm) AA; 10 x 25mm AA.
Complement: 1,437.

Development: The four ships of the Kongo class were completed in 1913–15 as conventional battlecruisers, with high speed and limited protection. They were, however, highly regarded in the Imperial Japanese Navy, and during the interwar period they underwent two major reconstructions. In the first, 1927–30, anti-torpedo bulges were fitted, the horizontal protection was increased (the total weight of armour rose from 6,502 tons to 10,313 tons), and the elevation of the main guns was increased from 30° to 43°; they were also reboilered, but the additional weight of protection resulted in a reduction in maximum speed from 27·5kt to 25·9kt.

The second reconstruction, 1933–40, was undertaken with a view to restoring the ships' former high speed. The original machinery was completely removed and replaced by new lightweight turbines and boilers. The original

Above: *Hiei* as she appeared in the early 1930s following demilitarisation. "Y" turret and the entire secondary armament were removed.

Below: *Kongo* as completed by Vickers in 1913.

horsepower was more than doubled, and the stern was lengthened by 26ft (8m) to give a higher length-to-beam ratio. They subsequently attained speeds in excess of 30kt, and were redesignated "fast battleships". The anti-aircraft armament was updated, a catapult was installed (three aircraft) and additional armour was fitted to the barbettes. *Hiei*, which had been demilitarised in 1929 under the terms of the Washington Treaty, was the last to undergo reconstruction. She was given new fire control arrangements and a bridge structure layout which served as a model for the Yamato class. ▶

Below: *Kirishima* in 1931, before she was reboilered and re-engined. During the 1930s she received additional horizontal protection, and the first two funnels were trunked together.

After this second reconstruction the Kongo class were no longer employed as part of the Japanese battle line, but were deployed with the carriers and the cruiser squadrons, a role for which their high speed made them admirably suited. They therefore saw more extensive employment in the Pacific War than any other class of Japanese battleship.

In December 1941 *Hiei* and *Kirishima* escorted the six Japanese fleet carriers to Pearl Harbor, while *Kongo* and *Haruna* were deployed in support of the Southern Force which was charged with operations against the Philippines, Malaya, Java and Sumatra. Following the near-elimination of the carrier striking force at Midway, *Hiei* and *Kirishima* were directed into the battle for Guadalcanal. In November 1942 *Hiei* was engaged in a night battle with American cruisers, was crippled by more than fifty 8in (203mm) shell hits, and was finished off by torpedo bombers the following morning. Two nights later

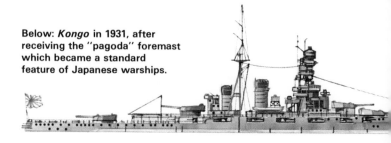

Below: *Kongo* in 1931, after receiving the "pagoda" foremast which became a standard feature of Japanese warships.

Below: *Kirishima* as she appeared in 1937, following her final modernisation. New boilers and turbine machinery were fitted, raising her speed to 30kt.

her sister, *Kirishima*, found herself engaged with the modern US battleships *Washington* and *South Dakota* at point blank range (8,400yds, 7,700m). She inflicted serious damage on *South Dakota* but was heavily hit by *Washington*, disabled by nine 16in (406mm) and more than forty 5in (127mm) shell hits, and had to be scuttled.

Kongo and *Haruna* survived until Leyte Gulf, when they were present with the Japanese battle force during the abortive strike against the American transport fleet. Neither ship received serious damage during the main action, but *Kongo* was sunk by a single torpedo from the US submarine *Sealion* off Formosa shortly after the Japanese withdrawal. Finally *Haruna* was sunk in shallow water by carrier aircraft near Kure in July 1945. Prior to these last battles *Kongo* and *Haruna* had their anti-aircraft armament increased to 12 x 5in (127mm) and 100 x 25mm; a further 18 x 25mm were later added to *Haruna*.

Below: ***Haruna*** **as she appeared in 1944. By this time considerable numbers of 25mm AA guns had been fitted, and an extra four 5in AA were carried. Note the Type 2 radar for surface search atop the "pagoda" mast.**

Fuso Class

Names: *Fuso, Yamashiro.*
Laid down: 1912–13.
Completed: 1915–17.
Reconstructed: 1930–35.
Displacement: 34,700 tons standard; 39,150 tons full load.
Dimensions: Length 698ft (212·8m) oa; beam 100ft 6in (30·6m) draught 31ft 9in (9·7m).
Propulsion: Kanpon geared steam turbines, 6 Kanpon boilers; 75,000shp; 4 shafts; 24·5kt.
Armour: Belt 12in–4in (305–100mm); deck 4in–2in (100–50mm); barbettes 8in (205mm) max; turrets 12in–4·5in (305–115mm); conning tower 13·75in (350mm) max.
Armament: 12 x 14in (356mm); 14 x 6in (152mm); 8 x 5in (127mm) AA; 16 x 25mm AA.
Complement: 1,396.

Development: When first completed, *Fuso* and *Yamashiro* epitomised the Japanese predilection for hitting power and mobility at the expense of protection. Both ships were, however, completely rebuilt in the 1930s, when they received improved horizontal protection and anti-torpedo bulges, and the total weight of armour was increased from 8,588 tons to 12,199 tons. New lightweight machinery was fitted, saving about 1,300 tons, and the stern was lengthened for higher speed. The elevation of the main armament was increased from 30° to 43°, and modern AA guns were fitted. The appearance of the ships was changed dramatically: the forefunnel was removed, and a massive "pagoda" bridge structure replaced the former tripod foremast. There was one catapult, and three aircraft could be carried.

Above: *Yamashiro* in 1930, before her final modernisation. Her foremast was rebuilt during the 1920s but she retained both funnels, the forefunnel being given a prominent cowling. *Fuso* was similarly refitted.

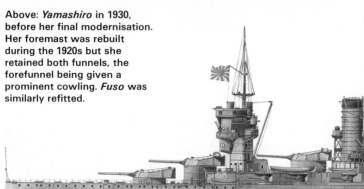

Above: *Fuso* after her final conversion. She and her sister were re-engined and reboilered for a top speed of 24·5kt.

The reconstruction appears not to have been a complete success. The ships were seriously overweight, and were relegated to second-line duties during World War II, when, together with *Ise* and *Hyuga*, they formed the 2nd Battleship Division. Following the Battle of Midway it was proposed to convert both ships to battleship-carriers on the lines adopted for *Ise* and *Hyuga*, but this proposal was not implemented, and they were eventually expended as a "decoy" force at Leyte Gulf. While attempting to transit the Surigao Strait they found their way blocked by the destroyers and old battleships of the American fire support force. Both ships were overwhelmed by a combination of torpedoes and 14in (356mm) and 16in (406mm) shellfire before sinking. This engagement was the last battleship-versus-battleship action to take place.

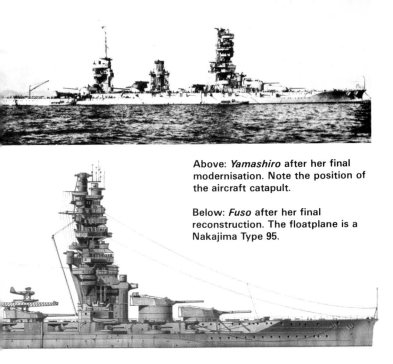

Above: *Yamashiro* after her final modernisation. Note the position of the aircraft catapult.

Below: *Fuso* after her final reconstruction. The floatplane is a Nakajima Type 95.

JAPAN

Ise Class

Names: *Ise, Hyuga.*
Laid down: 1915.
Completed: 1917–18.
Reconstructed: 1934–37, 1942–43.
Displacement: 35,800–36,000 tons standard; 40,170 tons full load.
Dimensions: Length 708ft (215·8m) oa; beam 104ft (31·7m); draught 30ft 2in (9·2m).
Propulsion: Kanpon geared steam turbines, 8 Kanpon boilers; 80,000shp; 4 shafts; 25·3kt.
Armour: Belt 12in–3in (305–75mm); decks 2in + 4·7in (50mm + 120mm); barbettes 12in (305mm) max; turrets 12in–8in (305–205mm); conning tower 12in–6in (305–155mm).
Armament: 12 x 14in (356mm); 16 x 5·5in (140mm); 8 x 5in (127mm) AA; 20 x 25mm AA.
Complement: 1,376.

Above: *Hyuga* in 1940, after her modernisation of 1934–37. Three Nakajima Type 95 floatplanes can be seen on the stern. The "pagoda" foremast was shorter than that of *Fuso*.

96

Development: *Ise* and *Hyuga* were designed as improved successors to the Fuso class. The major difference between the two classes as completed lay in the grouping together of the two midships 14in (356mm) turrets, which resulted in improved subdivision of the interior of the ship and made more space available for machinery. They were the first Japanese battleships to carry the new 5·5in (140mm) medium-calibre gun in place of the 6in (152mm) weapons previously mounted.

In a major reconstruction in 1934–37 they received modifications similar to those of the Fuso and Kongo classes. The machinery was completely renewed, the stern was lengthened by 24ft (7·6m), an anti-torpedo bulge was fitted, and the horizontal protection was improved (the total weight of armour increased from 9,525 tons to 12,644 tons). The elevation of the main guns was increased from 30^0 to 43^0 and that of the 5·5in (140mm) guns from 20^0 to 30^0, and new AA guns were fitted. The installation of new, lightweight, high-power boilers and turbines raised the maximum speed by 1·7kt and allowed a reduction to a single funnel, which was kept well clear of the new "pagoda" bridge structure. A catapult was fitted, handling three aircraft.

At the outbreak of war in the Pacific *Ise* and *Hyuga*, together with *Fuso* and ▶

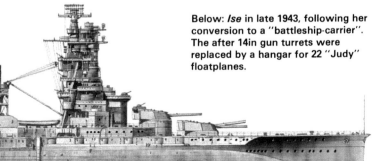

Below: *Ise* in late 1943, following her conversion to a "battleship-carrier". The after 14in gun turrets were replaced by a hangar for 22 "Judy" floatplanes.

Yamashiro, made up the 2nd Battleship Division. The division was deployed in support of the invasion of the Aleutians at the time of the Battle of Midway, but saw no action. Subsequently it was decided to convert *Ise* and *Hyuga* to hybrid battleship-carriers, and they were taken in hand in September 1942. They duly emerged in late 1943 with a much changed appearance. The conversion involved the removal of the after 14in (356mm) turrets and the construction in their place of a 200ft (60m) hangar topped by a flight deck for floatplanes. At the after end of the flight deck was a ''T''-shaped aircraft lift, and the aircraft were launched from two trainable catapults sited abreast the midships turrets. The medium-calibre battery was completely removed and replaced by a powerful AA armament which comprised 16 x 5in (127mm) and 57 x 25mm. In this guise they were to have carried 22 ''Judy'' dive-bombers but a chronic shortage both of aircraft and of pilots ensured that they were never to operate in their intended role. In October 1944, prior to the Battle of Leyte Gulf, the catapults were removed to free the arcs of the midships turrets. By this time the close-range AA armament had been increased to 108 x 25mm, of which a number of single mountings were located on the flight deck itself.

Ise and *Hyuga* made up the 4th Carrier Division at Leyte, but with few aircraft available they and the remaining first-line carriers could be used only as a decoy force to tempt Halsey's carrier task forces to the north, thereby enabling Vice-Admiral Kurita's main force of battleships and cruisers to break out through the San Bernadino Strait. Both ships were damaged by light bombs, but they survived to be sent to Kure for repairs in February 1945. There they were bombed in March, and then again in July, when they were sunk in shallow water. The hulls were broken up after the war.

Above: *Ise* running trials in 1943 following her conversion to a "battleship-carrier". During conversion the 5·5in guns of the secondary armament were removed and the AA armament was increased to 16 x 5in and 57 (later 108) 25mm guns.

Below: A ship of the Ise class under attack at the Battle of Leyte Gulf. Because of a shortage of aircraft and pilots the vessels never operated in their intended role, and in October 1944 the catapults were removed to provide better arcs for the midships 14in turrets and the ships were used as floating AA batteries.

Nagato Class

Names: *Nagato, Mutsu.*
Laid down: 1917–18.
Completed: 1920–21.
Reconstructed: 1934–36.
Displacement: 39,120 tons standard; 46,350 tons full load.
Dimensions: Length 738ft (224·9m) oa; beam 108ft 2in (33m); draught 31ft 2in (9·5m).
Propulsion: Kanpon geared steam turbines, 10 Kanpon boilers; 82,000shp; 4 shafts; 25kt.
Armour: Belt 11·8in–4in (300–100mm); decks 2·5in + 2·75in + 2in–3in (65mm + 70mm + 50–75mm); barbettes 11·8in + 4·9in (300mm + 125mm); turrets 14in (355mm) max; conning tower 14·6in–3·8in (370–95mm).
Armament: 8 x 16in (406mm); 18 x 5·5in (140mm); 8 x 5in (127mm) AA; 20 x 25mm AA.
Complement: 1,368.

Development: *Nagato* was the world's first 16in (406mm) gun battleship. She and her sister *Mutsu* were fast by the standards of the day, and were more heavily protected than their 14in (356mm) predecessors. They retained, however, the conventional dreadnought protection system of tapered armour belts and an elaborate combination of lightly plated decks in preference to the revolutionary "all or nothing" system pioneered by the US Navy.

Nagato and *Mutsu* were highly regarded in the Imperial Japanese Navy, and were thoroughly modernised from 1934 to 1936. Increased protection was given to the decks and the barbettes, bringing the total weight of armour up

Above: *Nagato* as she appeared in 1944, with large numbers of 25mm AA guns and Type 1 air search and Type 2 surface search radars.

from 10,396 tons to 13,032 tons. The propulsion machinery was also completely renewed and the stern lengthened by 28ft (8·7m), although horsepower was not increased as it had been in the older battleships, the Japanese being content to create a homogeneous 25kt battle-line. The superstructure was rebuilt on similar lines to the Fuso and Ise classes, and a modern anti-aircraft armament was fitted. There was a catapult, for three aircraft.

Like the Yamato class, with which they formed the 1st Battleship Division, *Nagato* and *Mutsu* had undistinguished combat careers. They were present at Midway, but contributed nothing to the battle. *Mutsu* was subsequently lost to an internal explosion in the Inland Sea in June 1943, but *Nagato* was present with Vice-Admiral Kurita's battle force at Leyte Gulf, where she received two torpedo and four bomb hits. Her close-range AA armament by this time comprised 98 x 25mm, two 5·5in .(140mm) guns having been removed in compensation. She survived to be expended in the postwar atom-bomb tests.

Below: *Nagato* photographed from a British warship at Tsingtao, China, in 1938. She had just undergone her final reconstruction, in which new boilers and turbines were fitted.

Yamato Class

Names: *Yamato, Musashi.*
Laid down: 1937–40.
Completed: 1941–42.
Displacement: 63,000 tons standard; 71,650 tons full load.
Dimensions: Length 862ft 9in (263m) oa; beam 121ft 1in (36·9m); draught 34ft 1in (10·4m).
Propulsion: Kanpon geared turbines, 12 Kanpon boilers; 150,000shp; 4 shafts; 27kt.
Armour: Belt 16in (410mm); deck 9in–8in (230–200mm); barbettes 21·5in + 2in (546mm + 50mm); turrets 25·6in–7·7in (650–193mm); conning tower 19·7in–11·8in (500–300mm); torpedo bulkhead 7·9in–3in (200–75mm).
Armament: 9 x 18·1in (460mm); 12 x 6·1in (155mm); 12 x 5in (127mm) AA; 24 x 25mm AA; 4 x 13·2mm AA.
Complement: 2,500.

Development: The largest and most powerful battleships ever completed, *Yamato* and her sistership *Musashi* were to have been the first in a series of "super-battleships" designed to wrest supremacy from the US Navy in the Pacific. It was estimated that battleships displacing more than 63,000 tons would be unable to transit the Panama Canal, and that by embarking on a programme of battleships of even greater displacement Japan would place the USA in the unenviable position of having either to build larger numbers of inferior ships, or to accept the political and military consequences of operating separate fleets in the Pacific and the Atlantic which could reinforce one another only with the greatest difficulty.

The construction in Japan of such large and powerful ships constituted an impressive technical achievement. When the final design was approved in March 1937 only the Mitsubishi Shipyard in Nagasaki had a slipway large enough to accommodate the hull, and this had to be reinforced. The other vessels of the class were laid down on slipways which were either newly

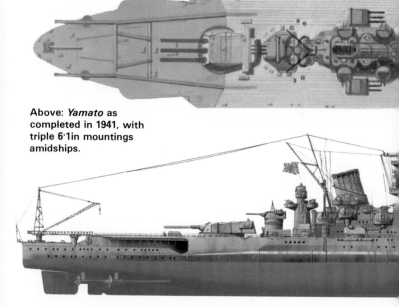

Above: *Yamato* as completed in 1941, with triple 6·1in mountings amidships.

Above: *Yamato* in September 1941, in the final stages of fitting out at Kure. A freighter had to be specially built to transport the massive 18·1in guns and triple turrets of the main armament to the shipyard. Construction took place in great secrecy to conceal the true size and power of these ships.

constructed or specially modified. The massive triple turrets and guns of the main armament were transported from the manufacturers to the shipyards aboard a purpose-built freighter. When assembled, these turrets each weighed 2,774 tons (2,818 tonnes), and the guns hurled shells weighing 3,240lb (1,470kg) over a distance of 45,300yds (41,400m).

Yamato and *Musashi* were built under the greatest secrecy. The slipways were shielded from prying eyes by massive sisal curtains, and the 46cm (18·1in) guns were officially designated "40·6cm Type 94" in order to deceive US Intelligence. The subterfuge and deception employed proved successful: ▶

Below: A striking feature of the Yamato class was the compact superstructure. The AA guns initially fitted were all above weather deck level.

Above: *Yamato* making 27kt during her official trial run in 1941. Note the undulating deck-line common in Japanese warships.

US Intelligence seriously underestimated both the displacement of *Yamato* and the calibre of her guns, and in the event none of the battleships laid down by the US Navy prior to the outbreak of war in the Pacific exceeded 45,000 tons, nor did they carry guns larger than 16in (406mm).

The protection of the Yamato class was designed on the "all or nothing" principle. A comparatively shallow side belt of 16in (410mm) armour, sloped to provide protection against 18in (457mm) shells, was topped by a thick armoured deck of 9–8in (230–200mm). There was a thin splinter deck beneath, but no "bomb deck" as in contemporary US Navy battleships. The underwater protection system was unique in having no liquid filling, and the ships had a remarkably shallow draught for their size — a reflection of the need to negotiate the shallow coastal waters of Japan.

The Imperial Japanese Navy, like many of the European navies, was reluctant to abandon the dedicated secondary "anti-destroyer" battery in favour of dual-purpose weapons, and *Yamato* and *Musashi* were completed with four triple 6·1in (155mm) turrets, disposed in a "lozenge" arrangement. As a result of war experience the two beam turrets were later removed, and replaced by additional anti-aircraft mountings. *Yamato* ended her career with an anti-aircraft armament of 24 x 5in (127mm), and no fewer than 150 x 25mm (29 x 3, 63 x 1). Two catapults serviced seven aircraft.

The maximum speed of 27kt was adequate for the fast battle-line planned by the Japanese, but was well below that of the latest fleet carriers, and the Navy was reluctant to employ *Yamato* and *Musashi* as carrier escorts, continuing to dream of the ultimate fleet gun engagement for which the ships had been ▶

Below: The low, narrow bow section resulted in considerable wetness forward when *Yamato* operated at high speed.

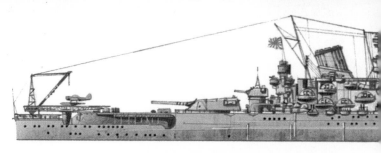

designed. *Yamato* headed the Japanese battleship force at Midway, but the defeat of Japan's carriers in that battle ensured that she would not be able to bring her big guns into action. Subsequently she and her newly completed sister *Musashi* spent much of the war at Truk, unable to intervene decisively in the island battles further south because of the weakness of Japanese carrier air power. *Yamato* was torpedoed by a US submarine in December 1943, and *Musashi* in March 1944, but both were repaired in time for the Battles of the Philippine Sea and Leyte Gulf. At Leyte (October 1944), the opportunity at last presented itself for the employment of the battleships in their intended role, and *Yamato* led a powerful force of battleships and cruisers through the San Bernadino Strait to destroy the American transport fleet, while the US carrier task forces and the fast battleships were engaged in a wild goose chase to the north. Had the attack been pressed home with more determination it might well have succeeded, but the Japanese battle force had been subjected to almost continuous air attacks for two days, and had already suffered crippling losses, including that of *Musashi,* which absorbed between eleven and nineteen torpedo hits and at least seventeen direct bomb hits before sinking. Vice-Admiral Kurita finally withdrew, having sunk only a small escort carrier and three destroyers. Finally, in April 1945, *Yamato* was sent out with a handful of destroyers on a suicide mission south-west of the Kyushu Islands, and was struck by between eleven and fifteen torpedoes and at least seven bombs before sinking.

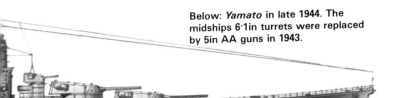

Below: *Yamato* in late 1944. The midships 6·1in turrets were replaced by 5in AA guns in 1943.

Two other ships the class were laid down. *Shinano* was completed as an aircraft carrier support ship in November 1944 and was sunk by six torpedoes from a US submarine whilst on her trials, and the construction of hull No. 111 was abandoned in November 1941 in order to free scarce shipyard resources for the carrier programme. Still larger battleships, mounting 20in (508mm) guns, were projected by the Imperial Japanese Navy, but these unrealistic vessels never proceeded beyond the planning stage.

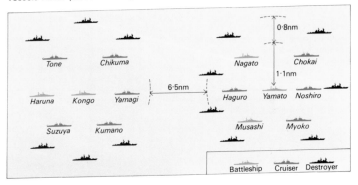

Tone   Chikuma   Nagato   Chokai

0·8nm

1·1nm

Haruna Kongo Yamagi   6·5nm   Haguro Yamato Noshiro

Suzuya Kumano   Musashi   Myoko

Battleship   Cruiser   Destroyer

Above: The Japanese battle force in anti-aircraft formation during its passage through the Sibuyan Sea. Vice-Admiral Kurita had already lost three powerful heavy cruisers, including his flagship *Atago*, to submarine attacks, and now flew his flag in *Yamato*. He was soon to lose her sister *Musashi*, crippled by US carrier aircraft, and most of his remaining heavy cruisers. In return he would sink only a small escort carrier, *Gambier Bay*, and three US destroyers, before abandoning the operation and returning to home waters.

Left: *Yamato* under aerial attack at the Battle of Leyte Gulf. The forward 18·1in turrets are trained to port. There are six twin 5in AA mountings to port and to starboard, with triple 25mm mountings at and above upper deck level.

Marat Class

Names: *Marat, Oktyabrskaya Revolutsiya, Parizhskaya Kommuna.*
Laid down: 1909.
Completed: 1914–15.
Displacement: 25,000–25,460 tons standard; 26,170–26,690 tons full load.
Dimensions: Length 606ft 6in (184·9m) oa; beam 88ft 3in/105ft (26·9m/32m); draught 30ft 6in–31ft 6in (9·3–9·6m).
Propulsion: Parsons steam turbines, 22–25 Yarrow boilers except *Oktyabrskaya Revolutsiya* 12 Yarrow–Normand boilers; 50,000–61,000shp; 4 shafts; 23kt.
Armour: Belt 8·8in–4in (225–100mm); decks 1·5in + 1·5in–1in (38mm + 37–25mm); barbettes 8in (205mm); turrets 8in–4·1in (205–105mm); conning tower 10in–5in (255–125mm).
Armament: 12 x 12in (305mm); 16 x 4·7in (120mm); 6 x 45mm AA; 16–24 x 13·2mm AA; 4 x 17·7in (450mm) torpedo tubes.
Complement: 1,277–1,400.

Below: *Oktyabrskaya Revolutsiya* (formerly *Gangut*) in the late 1930s. She was the only unit of the class to be reboilered.

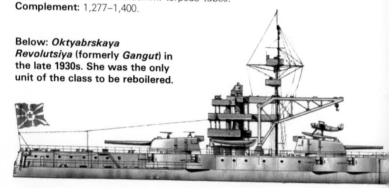

Development: These were the only Russian dreadnoughts to survive the Revolution of 1917. The philosophies of the Soviet Young School of the 1920s and 1930s did not favour the battleship, and the three vessels received only token modernisations during this period. The bridge and fire control arrangements were modified, and heavy cranes were fitted to handle the one or two aircraft and boats; no catapult was fitted. *Oktyabrskaya Revolutsiya*, and probably *Parizhskaya Kommuna*, were reboilered and the former ship may also have been re-engined, but *Marat* merely had her original boilers converted to oil-burning.

During World War II all three ships were employed primarily for fire support. *Oktyabrskaya Revolutsiya* and *Marat,* which served in the Baltic, bombarded Finnish shore positions in 1939–40. The rapid German advance into the USSR in 1941 compelled the Russians to withdraw them to Leningrad, where they engaged in action with German shore batteries. *Oktyabrskaya Revolutsiya* was damaged by gunfire in September, and *Marat* was bombed by Ju 87 dive-bombers and sank in shallow water. Her after turrets remained intact and she was subsequently employed as a stationary battery, being renamed *Petropavlovsk* in 1943. Her sistership was also damaged by German bombers in April 1942, and thereafter remained inactive for the rest of the war. *Parizhskaya Kommuna,* which served in the Black Sea, shelled German positions near Sevastopol in 1941–42, but following bomb damage sustained in German air attacks was withdrawn to Poti, where she remained unrepaired until the end of the war. She was renamed *Sevastopol* in 1943, and she and *Oktyabrskaya Revolutsiya* were scrapped in the mid-1950s.

Right: Another view of *Marat* at the Spithead Review. The theories of the Soviet Young School did not favour the battleship, and neither *Marat* nor her sisters were reconstructed.

Above: *Marat* at the Spithead Review of 1937. During the 1920s the forefunnel was angled back to keep the exhaust gases clear of the new tubular foremast/FC directors.

Kirov Class

Names: *Kirov, Frunze.*
Laid down: 1973–78.
Completed: 1980–83.
Displacement: 24,000 tons standard; 28,000 tons full load.
Dimensions: Length 814ft (248m); beam 92ft (28m); draught 29ft (8·8m).
Propulsion: CONAS, 2 nuclear reactors with oil-fired superheaters; 120,000shp; 2 shafts; 30kt.
Armour: Possibly around forward missile magazines.
Armament: 20 x SS-N-19 SSM launchers; 12 x SA-N-6 SAM launchers (96 missiles); 16 x SA-N-8 SAM launchers (96 missiles, *Frunze* only); 2 x SA-N-4 SAM launchers (40 missiles); 2 x 3·9in (100mm) DP in *Kirov*, 2 x 5·1in (130mm) DP in *Frunze*; 8 x 30mm Gatling guns; 2 x SS-N-14 ASW launchers (14–16 missiles, *Kirov* only); 1 x RBU 6000 ASW rocket launcher; 2 x RBU 1000 ASW rocket launchers; 8 x 21in (533mm) torpedo tubes.
Complement: 800.

Below: The long forecastle of *Kirov* houses the vertical launch tubes for her major weapons.

Above: Three ASW and missile guidance helicopters are carried in a hangar beneath the quarterdeck. The lift is forward of the helicopter landing pad.

Development: Classified by the Soviet Navy as a rocket cruiser, *Kirov* is regarded by many as a true descendent of the battlecruiser. In place of the big guns of her ancestors she has a powerful battery of 20 long-range SS-N-19 surface-to-surface missiles housed in a multi-cell vertical-launch box sunk into the forecastle. Targeting data would be supplied by a command post ashore via a communications satellite, or possibly directly by surveillance satellites using electronic intelligence (elint), active radar, or infra-red detection techniques. The missiles have a maximum range of 250–300nm (465–555km).

As the primary target would probably be a carrier battle group, *Kirov* is well provided with sophisticated air defence systems. The SA-N-6 surface-to-air missile is a new high-performance model, fired from rotating below-decks magazines located immediately forward of the SS-N-19 box. There are twelve rotating magazines, each with eight missiles, and a new track-via-missile (TVM) guidance system enables the cruiser to keep a number of missiles in the air simultaneously, ensuring the effective engagement of multiple targets. The missile itself is thought to have a range of more than 45nm (80,000m) and a speed of Mach 5–6.

The SA-N-6 system is backed up by two short-range SA-N-4 air defence systems, each comprising a "pop-up" launcher housed in a magazine bin containing 18–20 missiles, and two single 3·9in (100mm) guns. *Frunze*, the second ship of the class, has a twin 5·1in (130mm) mounting in place of the single 3·9in (100mm) guns, and also has vertical-launch tubes for a new short-range air defence system, which will probably be designated SA-N-8. Close- ▶

Left: Abreast the doors concealing the helicopter lift are two pairs of 30mm Gatling guns for anti-missile defence. *Kirov* (seen here) has two single 100mm DP mountings abaft the superstructure, but her sister *Frunze* has the new twin 130mm mounting first seen on the destroyers of the Sovremenny class.

range anti-missile defence in both ships comprises four groups each of two Gatling guns in the four "corners" of the ship.

Unlike earlier battlecruisers, these Soviet vessels are expected to conduct their own anti-submarine defence. *Kirov* has a reloadable launcher for SS-N-14 ASW missiles tucked inside the forecastle, and both ships have rocket launchers, torpedo tubes and three Ka-25 Hormone-A/B helicopters for ASW and for missile guidance. There is a large low-frequency bow sonar, and an LF variable-depth sonar is housed in the stern. The extensive electronics suite includes two major 3-D air surveillance radars, "Top Pair" and "Top Steer", plus individual gun and missile fire control radars.

TURKEY
Yavuz

Laid down: 1909.
Completed: 1912.
Displacement: 23,100 tons standard; 25,200 tons full load.
Dimensions: Length 610ft 3in (186m) oa; beam 96ft 9in (29·5m); draught 30ft 3in (9·2m).
Propulsion: Parsons direct-drive steam turbines, 24 Schultz-Thornycroft boilers; 52,000shp; 4 shafts; 25·5kt.
Armour: Belt 10·6in–4in (270–100mm); decks 1in + 2in (25mm + 50mm); barbettes 10in (250mm); turrets 9in–3·5in (230–90mm); conning tower 14in (350mm).
Armament: 10 x 11in (280mm); 10 x 5·9in (150mm); 4 x 3·5in (88mm); 4 x 3·5in (88mm) AA; 2 x 19·7in (500mm) torpedo tubes.
Complement: 1,300.

Below: *Yavuz* (formerly the German *Goeben*) as she appeared during World War I. She remained largely unmodified through two world wars, decommissioning only in 1960.

Below: An overhead view of *Kirov*. The SS-N-19 anti-ship missiles are housed in vertical-launch tubes; the twenty hatches covering the tubes can be seen immediately forward of the superstructure. The twin-tube launcher for SS-N-14 anti-submarine missiles can be seen tucked inside the break in the forecastle; the launcher is reloaded from magazine doors located immediately forward of it. Between the SS-N-14 tubes and the SS-N-19 hatches can be seen the twelve hatches concealing the rotating vertical-launch magazines for the SA-N-6 surface-to-air missiles. Each magazine ring contains eight missiles, for a total of 96. *Kirov* prompted the recommissioning of the US Iowas.

Development: Formerly the German battlecruiser *Goeben*, *Yavuz* remained virtually in her original condition until 1941, when 10 x 40mm and 4 x 20mm were fitted. Later the close-range AA was increased to 22 x 40mm and 24 x 20mm, the mainmast being removed to improve arcs of fire. *Yavuz* remained in commission until 1960 and was broken up in 1971.

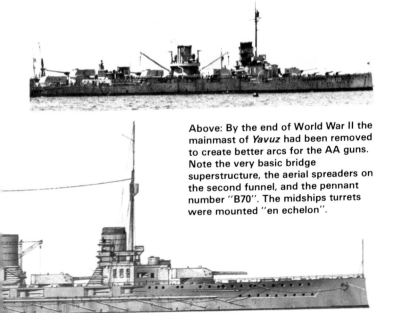

Above: By the end of World War II the mainmast of *Yavuz* had been removed to create better arcs for the AA guns. Note the very basic bridge superstructure, the aerial spreaders on the second funnel, and the pennant number "B70". The midships turrets were mounted "en echelon".

Arkansas Class

Laid down: 1910.
Completed: 1912.
Displacement: 26,100 tons standard; 31,000 tons full load.
Dimensions: Length 562ft (170·3m) oa; beam 106ft 3in (32·3m); draught 32ft (9·7m).
Propulsion: Parsons steam turbines, 4 White-Forster boilers; 28,000shp; 4 shafts; 20·5kt.
Armour: Belt 11in–5in (280–125mm); decks 2in + 3in (50mm + 75mm); barbettes 11in (280mm); turrets 12in–9in (305–230mm); conning tower 12in (305mm).
Armament: 12 x 12in (305mm); 16 x 5in (127mm); 8 x 3in (76mm) AA.
Complement: 1,330.

Above: A wartime view of *Arkansas*. She was employed mainly in Atlantic convoy escort from December 1941 until April 1944.

Development: *Arkansas* (BB33) and her sister *Wyoming* (BB32) were the last US battleships armed with 12in (305mm) guns. They were extensively refitted in 1925–27, when the original twelve coal-burning boilers were replaced by four oil-burning units. The second funnel was suppressed, the cage mainmast was replaced by a stump tripod, the horizontal protection was increased, and anti-torpedo bulges were fitted. The forward 5in (127mm) guns were resited on the upper deck to enable them to be worked in a seaway, 3in (76mm) AA guns were fitted, and a catapult (three aircraft) was installed.

In 1932 *Wyoming* was demilitarised, and *Arkansas* would undoubtedly have decommissioned had it not been for the outbreak of war in Europe in 1939. In a refit in 1940–41 the angle of elevation of the main guns was increased from 15⁰ to 30⁰.

In July 1941 *Arkansas* supported landing operations in Iceland, and from December 1941 until April 1944 was employed in convoy escort duties to and from the USA, Europe and North Africa. In a refit at New York Navy Yard from March to July 1942, all except six of her 5in (127mm) guns were removed, and the AA armament was increased to 10 x 3in (76mm), 32 x 40mm, and 26 x 20mm; at the same time the cage foremast was replaced by a tripod, and radar was fitted for surveillance and fire control.

Arkansas bombarded Cherbourg in support of the Normandy landings in June 1944, returning to the USA in September. She was subsequently transferred to the Pacific, and participated in the operations against Iwo Jima and Okinawa. She was finally expended as a target in the postwar atomic bomb tests.

Above: *Wyoming* as an AA gunnery ship during 1944. Her side armour and all main and secondary guns had been removed by this time, being replaced by 5in, 3in and 40mm AA guns.

Below: *Arkansas* in April 1944, by which time she bristled with 40mm and 20mm AA guns. She was deployed in support of the Normandy landings and later transferred to the Pacific.

New York Class

Names: *New York* (BB34), *Texas* (BB35).
Laid down: 1911.
Completed: 1914.
Displacement: 27,000 tons standard; 32,000 tons full load.
Dimensions: Length 573ft (174·7m) oa; beam 106ft 3in (32·4m); draught 31ft 6in (9·6m).
Propulsion: Reciprocating engines, 6 Bureau Express boilers; 28,100ihp; 2 shafts; 21kt.
Armour: Belt 12in–6in (305–150mm); decks 3·7in + 3in (95mm + 75mm); barbettes 12in (305mm); turrets 14in–8in (355–205mm); conning tower 12in (305mm).
Armament: 10 × 14in (356mm); 16 × 5in (127mm); 8 × 3in (76mm) AA.
Complement: 1,314.

Right: *New York* as she appeared between late 1942 and early 1944, during which period she and *Texas* were employed on convoy escort duties in the Atlantic and provided fire support for landing operations in the same theatre. *New York* participated in the destruction of the French battleship *Jean Bart* at Casablanca.

Development: The two battleships of the New York class were essentially improved Wyomings, with five twin 14in (356mm) turrets in place of the six 12in (305mm) turrets of the latter. A surprising feature of the class was the reversion to reciprocating machinery, which was apparently considered by the US Navy to be more economical at cruise speed than the steam turbines then in production.

In 1926 *New York* and *Texas* underwent a refit similar to that of the earlier ships, in which they were reboilered, received an AA armament of 3in (76mm) guns and a catapult (three aircraft), and had their cage masts replaced by tripods. By the late 1930s, however, these elderly vessels had been relegated to the training role, and it was only the outbreak of war in Europe which prompted further modernisation, again on the lines of *Arkansas*. In 1940–41 the elevation of the main guns was increased from 15° to 30°.

During 1942 and 1943 both ships were generally employed on convoy escort duty to and from the USA, Europe and North Africa. They provided fire support off Casablanca during the Allied invasion of French North Africa in November 1942, and *Texas* also participated in the landings in Normandy in June 1944, and in Southern France in August. By this time the close-range AA comprised 24 × 40mm and 36–42 × 20mm. Both ships were subsequently transferred to the Pacific, where they supported the landings on Iwo Jima and Okinawa. *New York* was damaged in a kamikaze attack and was finally expended as a target in the atomic bomb tests. *Texas* survived to become a museum ship, and she is now preserved in a permanent berth in the San Jacinto State Park, near Houston.

Above: *Texas* in April 1944, shortly before she deployed in support of the Normandy landings. She and *New York* later transferred to the Pacific.

Below: *Texas* in 1942, her AA armament boosted by large numbers of 40mms and 20mms.

Nevada Class

Names: *Nevada* (BB36), *Oklahoma* (BB37).
Laid down: 1912.
Completed: 1916.
Displacement: 29,070 tons standard; 34,000 tons full load.
Dimensions: Length 583ft (177·7m); beam 108ft (32·9m); draught 29ft 8in (9m).
Propulsion: Curtis steam turbines in *Nevada,* reciprocating engines in *Oklahoma;* 6 Bureau Express boilers; 26,500shp/24,800ihp; 2 shafts; 20·5kt.
Armour: Belt 13·5in–8in (345–205mm); decks 3in + 1·5in (75mm + 38mm); barbettes 13·5in (345mm); turrets 18in–5in (460–125mm); conning tower 16in (405mm).
Armament: 10 x 14in (356mm); 12 x 5in (127mm); 8 x 5in (127mm) AA.
Complement: 1,301.

Above: Struck by one torpedo and five bombs at Pearl Harbor, *Nevada* was raised in February 1942 and towed to Puget Sound Navy Yard on the West Coast, where she was completely rebuilt. The secondary battery was removed and replaced by a modern AA armament of 5in/38cal. guns, backed up by quadruple 40mm AA guns.

Above: *Nevada* as she appeared in April 1937. Her former cage masts had by this time been replaced by massive tripods. *Nevada* was the first battleship to have the "all or nothing" protection system, and the first US battleship with triple turrets.

Development: *Nevada* was the world's first battleship with "all or nothing" protection. The length of the armoured citadel was reduced by the adoption of triple turrets and oil-fired boilers. The machinery arrangement was particularly compact compared with that of her predecessors, requiring only a single funnel. *Nevada* was given steam turbines, but her sister *Oklahoma* was the last US battleship to have reciprocating machinery.

In 1927–29 both ships were extensively refitted. The original boilers were replaced, tripods were installed in place of the former cage masts, the horizontal protection was increased, and anti-torpedo bulges were fitted. The elevation of the main guns was increased from 15° to 30°, the secondary battery was re-sited one deck higher, and new AA guns were fitted. Two catapults could service three aircraft.

Nevada and *Oklahoma* were both at Pearl Harbor in December 1941. *Oklahoma* capsized after being struck by four torpedoes and, although salvaged in 1943, she was never repaired. *Nevada* was struck by one airborne torpedo and four bombs; she settled on the bottom, but was later raised and rebuilt at Puget Sound Navy Yard. She recommissioned in the spring of 1943 with a much-changed appearance. Her original secondary and AA batteries were removed and replaced by a new dual-purpose battery of 16 x 5in (127mm)/38cal. guns in twin turrets. The superstructure was rebuilt to improve the arcs of these guns, and 36 x 40mm and 38 x 20mm were added. Following escort duties between the USA and Britain *Nevada* provided fire support for the landings in Normandy and in Southern France in 1944. She was then transferred to the Pacific, where she supported the landings on Iwo Jima and Okinawa. She was expended as a target postwar.

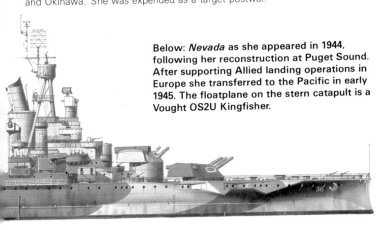

Below: *Nevada* as she appeared in 1944, following her reconstruction at Puget Sound. After supporting Allied landing operations in Europe she transferred to the Pacific in early 1945. The floatplane on the stern catapult is a Vought OS2U Kingfisher.

Pennsylvania Class

Names: *Pennsylvania* (BB38), *Arizona* (BB39).
Laid down: 1913–14.
Completed: 1916.
Displacement: 33,100/32,600 tons standard; 36,500 tons full load.
Dimensions: Length 608ft (185·3m) oa; beam 106ft 3in (32·4m); draught 30ft 3in (9·2m).
Propulsion: Curtis/Parsons steam turbines, 6 Bureau Express boilers; 33,750shp; 4 shafts; 21kt.
Armour: Belt 14in–8in (355–205mm); decks 4in + 2in (100mm + 50mm); barbettes 14in (355mm); turrets 18in–5in (460–125mm); conning tower 16in (405mm).
Armament: 12 x 14in (356mm); 12 x 5in (127mm); 8 x 5in (127mm) AA.
Complement: 1,358.

Below: *Pennsylvania* **at Lingayen Gulf in January 1945. The barrels of the 5in/38cal. guns fitted in 1943 are pointing skywards.**

Above: *Pennsylvania* as she appeared in 1943, following a major refit in which new AA guns and fire control radars were fitted.

Below: *Pennsylvania* in dry dock during World War II. Nearly all battleships of World War I vintage were fitted with anti-torpedo bulges during the 1920s and 1930s. The bulges were designed to absorb the effects of an underwater explosion, and also provided buoyancy and stability in ships which had received large quantities of armour for improved horizontal protection.

Development: These two ships were a logical development of the Nevada class, with a heavier main battery in four triple turrets and improvements in protection. Both were refitted in 1929–31 on similar lines to the Nevadas. They were reboilered, the horizontal protection was improved, and heavy tripods replaced the former cage masts. The elevation of the main guns was increased from 15° to 30°, the 5in (127mm) secondary battery was re-sited at forecastle deck level, and eight 5in (127mm) AA guns were fitted. The ships received four additional 5in (127mm) AA mountings in 1940.

Pennsylvania and *Arizona* were both present at Pearl Harbor in December 1941. *Arizona* was struck by one torpedo and eight bombs, and sank in shallow water following a magazine explosion. She was never raised and in 1962 became a national memorial. *Pennsylvania*, which was in dry dock at the time of the attack, was hit by a single bomb which caused moderate damage. Following repair she was employed briefly on escort and training duties off the West Coast of the USA before entering Mare Island Navy Yard in October 1942 for rebuilding. She emerged in 1942 with a completely new dual-purpose secondary battery of 16 x 5in (127mm)/38cal. guns, and a close-range AA armament of 40 x 40mm and about 50 x 20mm. In this guise *Pennsylvania* provided fire support for virtually all the major amphibious landings in the Pacific from November 1943 until October 1944, when she participated in the sinking of the Japanese battleships *Fuso* and *Yamashiro* in the Battle of Surigao Strait. In August 1945 she was seriously damaged by an airborne torpedo off Wake Island. She was towed to the West Coast for repair but was eventually expended as a target in the postwar atom-bomb tests.

New Mexico Class

Names: *New Mexico* (BB40), *Mississippi* (BB41), *Idaho* (BB42).
Laid down: 1915.
Completed: 1917–19.
Displacement: 33,000–33,400 tons standard; 35,100–36,150 tons full load.
Dimensions: Length 624ft (190·2m) oa; beam 97ft 5in (29·7m); draught 34ft (10·4m).
Propulsion: Westinghouse geared steam turbines, 6 Bureau Express boilers (4 White-Forster in *New Mexico*); 40,000shp; 4 shafts; 21·5kt.
Armour: Belt 14in–8in (355–205mm); decks 6in + 4in (150mm + 100mm); barbettes 14in (355mm); turrets 18in–5in (460–125mm); conning tower 16in (405mm).
Armament: 12 x 14in (356mm); 12 x 5in (127mm); 8 x 5in (127mm) AA.
Complement: 1,323.

Development: In this class the general design of the *Pennsylvania* was adhered to, but improved features included a new 14in (356mm) gun and enhanced internal protection. *New Mexico* introduced turbo-electric propulsion to the US Navy, but all three ships of the class were re-boilered and re-engined during major refits from 1931 to 1934. The horizontal protection was improved, anti-torpedo bulges were fitted, the original cage masts were replaced by a modern tower bridge structure with a light pole mainmast, and 5in (127mm) AA guns were fitted.

All three ships were in the Atlantic at the time of Pearl Harbor and as they were the most up-to-date of the older US battleships they received few further modifications. Between 36 and 56 x 40mm and 14–44 x 20mm were added, and

Above: A prewar view of *New Mexico* following her reconstruction in the early 1930s. These were the only US battleships to receive a thorough modernisation before World War II. The machinery was completely renewed and a British-style "tower" foremast was fitted.

Above: *Mississippi* at speed, displaying the revised superstructure and fire control arrangements which date from her 1931-32 refit. Note the catapult atop "X" turret, later removed.

Mississippi had six additional 5in (127mm)/25cal. AA guns fitted, but *Idaho* was the only ship to receive a modern dual-purpose secondary battery, comprising 10 x 5in (127mm)/38cal. guns in single turrets.

During 1942 *New Mexico, Mississippi* and *Idaho* were transferred to the Pacific, where they saw extensive service in support of amphibious landings beginning with the Aleutians campaign of May–July 1943. *Mississippi* was present at the Battle of Surigao Strait at Leyte Gulf. All three ships sustained moderate damage as a result of kamikaze and conventional air attacks in the final months of the war. *New Mexico* and *Idaho* were subsequently sold for scrap, but *Mississippi* was employed as a missile trials ship from 1952 to 1956, and had prototype Terrier launchers installed aft.

Above: "X" and "Y" turrets are trained to port in this late war view of a New Mexico class battleship. Atop the starboard catapult is a Vought OS2U.

Below: *Mississippi* in January 1945, as she appeared off Luzon.

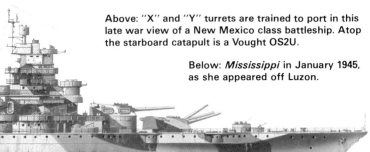

California Class

Names: *California* (BB44), *Tennessee* (BB43).
Laid down: 1916–17.
Completed: 1920–21.
Displacement: 32,600/32,300 tons standard; 35,190 tons full load.
Dimensions: Length 624ft 6in (190·4m) oa; beam 97ft 3in (29·7m); draught 35ft (10·7m).
Propulsion: Curtis/Westinghouse turbines with turbo-electric drive, 8 Bureau Express/Babcock & Wilcox boilers; 28,500ehp; 4 shafts; 21kt.
Armour: Belt 14in–8in (355–205mm); decks 3·5in + 2in (90mm + 50mm); barbettes 14in (355mm); turrets 18in–5in (460–125mm); conning tower 16in (405mm).
Armament: 12 x 14in (356mm); 12 x 5in (127mm); 8 x 5in (127mm) AA.
Complement: 1,480.

Above: *Tennessee* following reconstruction. Her super-structure was remodelled on the lines of the South Dakota class, and a new dual-purpose secondary battery of 5in/38cal. guns in twin turrets was fitted. There were forty 40mm guns in quadruple mountings. The large air surveillance radar is an SK.

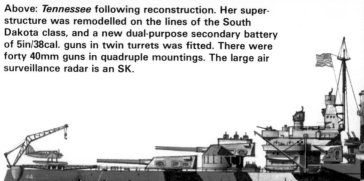

Development: The California class was a repeat of the New Mexico type, but with a number of important modifications. The hull was flush-sided because the secondary battery was designed from the outset to be mounted at forecastle level, and further improvements were made in the internal subdivision of the ships. Long-running arguments in the US Navy regarding the relative merits of the various propulsion systems available resulted in the final adoption of turbo-electric machinery for these ships and their near-sisters of the Maryland class. Steam was produced in eight boiler rooms for two 15,000kVA turbo-alternators, which in turn powered four 4,300kV electric motors, each of which was directly coupled to one of the four shafts. Because of the potential vulnerability of turbo-electric transmission to action damage the turbo-alternators and auxiliary electrical machinery were inside the boiler rooms, each of which was designed as a watertight compartment. The arrangement of the boiler rooms dictated a return to twin funnels. Turbo-electric propulsion had a number of advantages over steam turbine propulsion, of which the most important were the elimination of the need for separate astern turbines ▶

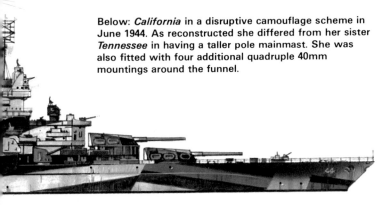

Below: *California* in a disruptive camouflage scheme in June 1944. As reconstructed she differed from her sister *Tennessee* in having a taller pole mainmast. She was also fitted with four additional quadruple 40mm mountings around the funnel.

and the ease with which power could be redistributed to all four shafts in the event of boiler or turbo-alternator failure. The major disadvantages were the weight and bulk of the machinery and the vulnerability of turbo-electric transmission to action damage — which led to the abandonment of this form of propulsion in the fast battleships designed in the 1930s.

A modern anti-aircraft battery was installed in the 1920s and a pair of catapults (3–4 aircraft) was added, but although funds were approved in 1939 for a more complete modernisation, the political situation made it imperative that *California* and *Tennessee* be maintained in a state of readiness. Both were at Pearl Harbor in December 1941. *Tennessee* sustained only moderate damage from two bomb hits, and after repair remained at Hawaii until she was taken in hand for rebuilding at Puget Sound Navy Yard in September 1942. *California*, however, was struck by two torpedoes and three bombs, and sank in shallow water; she was raised in March 1942 and towed to Puget Sound for rebuilding.

The reconstruction of these two units was particularly thorough. They received additional horizontal protection, and massive anti-torpedo bulges extending from the ship's bottom to the upper deck were fitted. The additional deck space thus created was used to provide a modern AA armament of 16 x 5in (127mm)/38cal. DP guns, 56/40 x 40mm, and 48/52 x 20mm. The superstructure was completely rebuilt on the lines of the South Dakota class, with a broad single funnel faired into a tower foremast and a light pole mainmast.

Tennessee recommissioned in May 1943, and was immediately deployed in the Aleutians campaign. *California,* because of the extensive damage sustained at Pearl Harbor, did not re-enter service until January 1944. Both ships provided fire support for the amphibious landings in the Pacific; both sustained slight damage from Japanese coastal batteries off Saipan in August 1944; and both participated in the Battle of Surigao Strait at Leyte Gulf. *California* was hit by a kamikaze in January 1945 off Luzon, and *Tennessee* was damaged in a similar attack while operating off Okinawa in April. At the end of the war they were placed in reserve as part of the "mothball fleet", and were finally sold for breaking up in 1959.

Above: *Tennessee* off Okinawa in April 1945, her big guns trained to starboard; note the massive beam of these ships and the single 20mm Oerlikons dotted around the superstructure.

Below: *Tennessee* fires her 14in guns at shore positions on Okinawa as the landing craft go ashore. Both ships of the class were employed in fire support following reconstruction.

USA
Maryland Class

Names: *Colorado* (BB45), *Maryland* (BB46), *West Virginia* (BB48).
Laid down: 1917–20.
Completed: 1921–23.
Displacement: 31,500–32,500 tons standard; 39,100–40,400 tons full load.
Dimensions: Length 624ft (190·2m) oa; beam 97ft 6in (29·7m); draught 35ft (10·7m).
Propulsion: Westinghouse/Curtis turbines with turbo-electric drive, 8 Babcock & Wilcox boilers; 28,900ehp; 4 shafts; 21kt.
Armour: Belt 16in–8in (405–205mm); decks 3·5in + 2in (90mm + 50mm); barbettes 16in–14in (405–355mm); turrets 18in–5in (460–125mm); conning tower 16in (405mm).
Armament: 8 x 16in (406mm); 12 x 5in (127mm); 8 x 5in (127mm) AA.
Complement: 1,407.

Development: The three battleships of the Maryland class (a fourth ship, *Washington*, had to be scrapped when almost complete as part of the terms of the Washington Treaty) were identical in many respects to *Tennessee* and *California*, with which they were generally grouped. The US Navy referred to these ships as the "Big Five", and they constituted the core of the Pacific Fleet when the Japanese attacked at Pearl Harbor. The major difference between the two types was the substitution of twin 16in (406mm) turrets for the triple 14in (356mm) turrets of the California class to counter the Japanese battleships of the Nagato class, which had been laid down in 1916–17. The thickness of the main belt was increased accordingly to withstand the heavier shell.

As with the Californias, they remained largely unaltered between the wars, receiving only a modern anti-aircraft armament and aircraft-handling facilities (two catapults, three aircraft) during refits in the 1920s. In 1939 funds were approved for a complete modernisation, but this was delayed by the onset of war in Europe. *Colorado* was taken in hand in June 1941, but with the outbreak of war in the Pacific she was hurriedly returned to service without any of the major modifications planned. ▶

Above: *West Virginia* and *Tennessee* following the Japanese attack on Pearl Harbor. *Tennessee* received only moderate damage from two bomb hits, but *West Virginia,* outboard of her, was struck by two bombs and no fewer than six torpedoes and sank in shallow water. Both ships were subsequently rebuilt on modern lines.

Below: *West Virginia* as she appeared prewar, with slim funnels and two tall, distinctive cage masts. Note the clipper stem.

Maryland and *West Virginia* were both present at Pearl Harbor at the time of the Japanese attack. *Maryland* sustained only moderate damage from two bomb hits, and was back in service by February 1942, but *West Virginia* was less fortunate and sank in shallow water after being struck by six torpedoes and two bombs. Because of her relative modernity she was salvaged in May 1942, and proceeded to Puget Sound Navy Yard where she underwent a total reconstruction on the lines of *California* and *Tennessee*. Massive anti-torpedo bulges were fitted, which increased her beam to 114ft (34·8m). Her superstructure was remodelled on the lines of the new battleships of the South Dakota class, and a new dual-purpose battery of 16 x 5in (127mm)/38cal. guns in twin turrets was installed, backed up by 40 x 40mm and 50 x 20mm.

Maryland and *Colorado* received only piecemeal modification during the war. Horizontal protection was increased and standard anti-torpedo bulges were fitted during routine refits. Both ships had their secondary battery reduced to ten 5in (127mm) guns in 1942, and the older 5in (127mm)/25cal. AA were replaced by the more modern 5in (127mm)/38cal. model, although turrets for the latter were not available until late in the war, and they were fitted with temporary shields. A close-range AA armament of 16 x 40mm and 32 x 20mm was fitted, modified at a later stage to 40 x 40mm and about 18 x 20mm. The cage mainmast was initially cut down and used as a platform for light AA guns but was later replaced by a short tower with a pole mast.

Below: *Colorado* in April 1944. The cage mainmast had been removed by this time, and she carried eight single 5in/38cal. DP guns behind shields.

Colorado and *Maryland* were employed on general escort duties in 1942–43, and were also deployed to the South Pacific to guard Fiji and the New Hebrides against Japanese attacks. From November 1943 they provided fire support for amphibious landings. *Maryland* was damaged by an airborne torpedo off Saipan in June 1944, and *Colorado* was seriously damaged by Japanese coastal batteries while operating off Tinian in July 1944 and was under repair until November. In the same month, however, *West Virginia* recommissioned, and she and *Maryland* participated in the Battle of Surigao Strait at Leyte Gulf. All three ships sustained moderate damage from kamikazes during 1945, and *Maryland* received a new dual-purpose secondary battery of 16 x 5in (127mm)/38cal. guns in twin turrets while under repair. After the war the class was placed in reserve, and all three ships were sold for scrap in 1959.

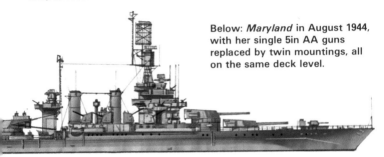

Below: *Maryland* in August 1944, with her single 5in AA guns replaced by twin mountings, all on the same deck level.

North Carolina Class

Names: *North Carolina* (BB55), *Washington* (BB56).
Laid down: 1937–38.
Completed: 1941.
Displacement: 37,500 tons standard; 44,400 tons full load.
Dimensions: Length 728ft 9in (222·1m) oa; beam 108ft 4in (33m); draught 33ft (10m).
Propulsion: General Electric geared steam turbines, 8 Babcock & Wilcox boilers; 121,000shp; 4 shafts; 28kt.
Armour: Belt 12in–6·6in (305–165mm); decks 1·5in + 5·5in (38mm + 140mm); barbettes 16in–14·7in (405–375mm); turrets 16in–7in (405–180mm); conning tower 16in–7in (405–180mm).
Armament: 9 x 16in (406mm); 20 x 5in (127mm) DP; 16 x 1·1in (28mm) AA.
Complement: 1,880.

Development: *North Carolina* and her sister *Washington* were the first US capital ships to be laid down after the expiry of the "battleship holiday" imposed by the Washington Treaty. Although design work was begun in the early 1930s, the United States waited to see what sort of ships would be laid down by Britain and Japan before deciding on the final configuration.

The first design sketches were for an updated version of the traditional US battleship, with firepower and protection emphasised at the expense of speed. In 1935, however, the General Board was compelled to look more closely at the fast battleships then being laid down in Europe. The issue was finally decided by the need for the ships to operate with aircraft carriers.

A 30kt design with 9 x 14in (356mm) guns was initially proposed, but this was rejected in favour of a ship with less speed (27kt) but more firepower (11, later 12, 14in, 356mm, guns). However, when the Japanese refused to be bound by the 14in (356mm) limit, the United States invoked the "Escalator Clause", and the main armament was altered to 9 × 16in (406mm) in triple turrets. The design displacement still had to be kept within the 35,000-ton limit, so it was not possible to upgrade protection accordingly, and the ships were armoured only against 14in (356mm) shellfire. ▶

Right: A bow view of *North Carolina*, probably taken in 1945. The air surveillance radar is an SK-2.

Below: *North Carolina* underway in mid-1944. This ship is carrying a disruptive camouflage scheme.

The protection system continued to be based on the "all or nothing" principle, but with some modifications. The side belt was sloped, and there was 1·5in (38mm) "burster" plating on the upper deck to prevent bombs and plunging shells from penetrating the main amoured deck. New, lightweight steam turbines were adopted to provide the ships with the high speed required, and a "unit" machinery arrangement ensured that the effects of action damage would be limited. For the first time in US battleship construction a dual-purpose secondary armament, comprising 20 x 5in (127mm) guns of a new 38cal. model, was mounted. The quadruple 1·1in (28mm) mountings fitted at completion were replaced in late 1942 by 40 x 40mm and up to 54 x 20mm. By 1943 the number of 40mm had risen to 52–60, and *Washington* ended the war with 96. Two catapults were fitted, for three aircraft.

**Below: *North Carolina* in June 1942.
As completed her only light AA
weapons were four quadruple 1·1in.**

North Carolina and *Washington* commissioned shortly before the outbreak of war in the Pacific, but were not ready for service until the spring of 1942. In March *Washington* was detached to the British Home Fleet and was employed on escort duties for the Murmansk convoys, being transferred to the Pacific only in June. Both ships entered action immediately in the Solomons area. In September *North Carolina* was present at the Battle of the Eastern Solomons, but was subsequently struck by a torpedo from the submarine *I15* while in company with the carrier *Wasp*, which was sunk in the same attack. In November *Washington,* in company with the new battleship *South Dakota*, sank the Japanese battleship *Kirishima* in a fierce night action off Guadalcanal.

Above: *Washington* in November 1943, by which
time she had received large numbers of 40mm and
20mm AA guns. Although their design was
constrained by Treaty limitations, these ships proved
more successful in service than the South Dakotas.

From November 1943 both ships joined the fast carrier task forces in the
"island-hopping" campaign, providing anti-aircraft protection for the carriers
and fire support for the amphibious forces. They participated in the Battle of
the Philippine Sea, and were present during the final carrier raids on Japan.

Washington was placed in reserve after the war, and was sold for scrap in
1960. *North Carolina* became a training ship for a short period, and in 1961
became a national memorial in the state whose name she bore.

Below: *North Carolina* in April 1942. She is about to launch a Vought
OS2U Kingfisher floatplane from the starboard catapult.

USA

South Dakota Class

Names: *South Dakota* (BB57), *Indiana* (BB58), *Massachusetts* (BB59), *Alabama* (BB60).
Laid down: 1939–40.
Completed: 1942.
Displacement: 38,000 tons standard; 44,500 tons full load.
Dimensions: Length 680ft (207·3m) oa; beam 108ft 2in (33m); draught 35ft 1in (10·7m).
Propulsion: General Electric geared steam turbines, 8 Babcock & Wilcox boilers; 130,000shp; 4 shafts; 27·5kt.
Armour: Belt 12·25in (310mm); decks 1·5in + 6in (38mm + 150mm); barbettes 17·3in–11·3in (440–285mm); turrets 18in–7·25in (455–185mm); conning tower 16in–7·25in (405–185mm).
Armament: 9 x 16in (406mm); 20/16 x 5in (126mm) DP; 24/32 x 40mm AA; 30–56 x 20mm AA.
Complement: 1,793.

Development: The South Dakota class was an attempt to achieve adequate protection against 16in (406mm) shellfire while retaining the firepower of the North Carolina type and without exceeding the 35,000-ton displacement limit prescribed by the Washington Treaty. This involved a number of design compromises, resulting in a cramped ship which was inferior in many respects to the *North Carolina*. The enhanced protection was obtained by adopting a thicker side belt, the additional weight of which had to be compensated for by a reduction in the length of the citadel. In order to achieve this a more compact machinery layout was adopted, and the overall length of these ships was reduced by 50ft (15m) as compared with their predecessors, while beam remained unchanged. An ironic consequence of this reduction in fineness was that it was necesssary to increase installed horsepower by 9,000shp to enable them to achieve the same maximum speed as the North Carolinas.

The protection system showed a number of important modifications. Concern had been expressed regarding the vulnerability of the North Carolinas to plunging shells which penetrated beneath (or were deflected downwards by) their sloped side belts. The heavy sloped belt of the South Dakotas was therefore internal, and was continued down to the ship's inner bottom at a reduced thickness to provide protection for the ships' vitals. Anti-torpedo protection comprised three longitudinal bulkheads with the tapered lower end of the belt inside them to form an inner bulkhead. This system was not tested ▶

Right: An impressive aerial view of *Alabama* in August 1943. The aircraft-handling arrangements were standard to all US battleships completed from 1941 onwards. Note the compact layout of the 5in/38 cal. dual-purpose mountings amidships.

Below: *Alabama* in January 1943 in a disruptive camouflage scheme. Her first deployment was with the British Home Fleet.

before the ships were laid down, and the results from later testing of a purpose-built caisson gave cause for some concern. Unlike the North Carolinas, the South Dakotas were not bulged, and this meant that there was inadequate depth between the outer hull and the inner bulkhead, which because of its rigidity could not deform to absorb the shock of the explosion. The tests prompted some revision of the liquid loading arrangements, but the defect could not have been eliminated without major redesign.

The compactness of the machinery layout resulted in an equally compact superstructure arrangement. A large single funnel was faired into a tower foremast; arcs for the anti-aircraft guns were thereby improved at the cost of reduced superstructure volume. *South Dakota*, which was designed as a flagship, had an extra bridge level, which had to be compensated for by a reduction in the number of 5in (127mm) DP guns from 20 to 16 (the centre turret being omitted on each side); she was to have mounted additional quadruple 1·1in (28mm) mountings in these positions, but they were replaced by quadruple 40mm at completion.

Only two ships of the class were initially ordered, design work on their successors of the Iowa class commencing under the designation "BB59". However, with the world political situation deteriorating rapidly, a Deficiency Appropriations Act of June 1938 authorised two further units, and these were ordered as *Massachusetts* (BB59) and *Alabama* (BB60). As designed they would have carried 12 (20 in *South Dakota*) 1·1in (28mm) AA guns in quadruple mountings, plus twelve single 0·5in (12·7m) machine guns. In the event, however, these weapons were never fitted, and the ships received 24–32 x 40mm and 30–56 x 20mm at completion. During the latter part of the war close-range AA was further increased and by 1945 comprised 48–72 x 40mm and 37–72 x 20mm. A pair of catapults could handle three aircraft.

Above: *Massachusetts* in early 1945, when she took part in the carrier raids on Formosa and Tokyo. The South Dakota class were employed in identical fashion to the North Carolinas, as floating AA batteries and fire support ships. Note the tall mainmast fitted in this unit.

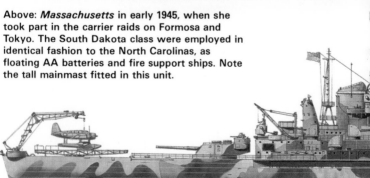

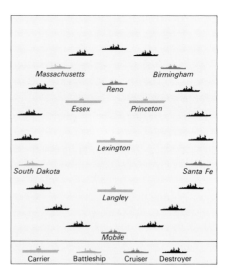

Right: The formation of Task Group 38.3 at Leyte Gulf in November 1944. The primary unit of organisation in the US Navy was the fleet (here the 3rd); a fleet was composed of a number of task forces (at Leyte the carriers made up Task Force 8); and each task force was subdivided into task groups — hence the designation Task Group 38.3. The modern battleships provided anti-aircraft protection for the carriers, but could be detached for surface engagements.

Massachusetts   Birmingham
Reno
Essex   Princeton
Lexington
South Dakota   Santa Fe
Langley
Mobile

Carrier   Battleship   Cruiser   Destroyer

On completion the first two ships, *South Dakota* and *Indiana*, were despatched to the Pacific. *South Dakota* was present at the Battle of Santa Cruz in October 1942, when she claimed a total of 26 aircraft shot down and received one bomb hit in return. In company with *Washington*, she subsequently sank the Japanese battleship *Kirishima* in a night battle off Guadalcanal in November, but was badly mauled, sustaining no fewer than 42 hits from large- and small-calibre shell. After repairs in the United States she was detached to the British Home Fleet for a brief period in mid-1943 and was employed on convoy escort duties, returning to the Pacific in September.

Massachusetts and *Alabama* began their service careers in the Atlantic. *Massachusetts* provided support for the landings in French North Africa in November 1942, setting the battleship *Jean Bart* ablaze at Casablanca. *Alabama* was deployed in support of the Murmansk convoys in the spring and summer of 1943, but by autumn all four ships of the class were back in the Pacific in readiness for the US Navy's assault on the Japanese-held island chains. They were employed as fast carrier escorts and for fire support throughout 1944 and 1945. Three ships of the class were present at the Battle of the Philippine Sea, and three of the four were at Leyte; all four participated in the final carrier raids on Japan.

The South Dakota class was placed in reserve in 1946–47, and although various proposals were put forward for conversion to missile ships and amphibious support vessels, none was taken up. *South Dakota* and *Indiana* were sold for scrap in 1962–63, but *Massachusetts* and *Alabama* were preserved.

Below: *Indiana* in April 1942, shortly after completion. The camouflage scheme was adopted for operations among the islands of the South Pacific. Note the compact superstructure.

139

USA
Iowa Class

Names: *Iowa* (BB61), *New Jersey* (BB62), *Missouri* (BB63), *Wisconsin* (BB64).
Laid down: 1940–42.
Completed: 1943–44.
Displacement: 48,110 tons standard; 57,540 tons full load.
Dimensions: Length 887ft 3in (270·43m) oa; beam 108ft 2in (33m); draught 36ft 3in (11·02m).
Propulsion: General Electric geared steam turbines, 8 Babcock & Wilcox boilers; 200,000shp; 4 shafts; 32·5kt.
Armour: Belt 12·25in (310mm); decks 1·5in + 4·7in + 5·5in (38mm + 120mm + 140mm); barbettes 17·3in–11·6in (440–295mm); turrets 19·7in–7·25in (495–185mm); conning tower 17·5in–7·25in (445–185mm).
Armament: 9 x 16in (406mm); 20 x 5in (127mm) DP; 60/80 x 40mm AA; 49–60 x 20mm AA.
Complement: 1,921.

Development: Although some of the earlier design sketches for the North Carolina class had been based on a requirement for the ships to be able to operate with the fast carriers, it did not prove possible to design a 30kt battleship with sufficient firepower and protection within the 35,000-ton displacement allowed by the Washington Treaty, and the final design for these ships and for their successors of the South Dakota class represented a compromise solution, with heavy firepower, adequate protection and a maximum speed of 27–28kt. Not until 1938, when rumours of the construction in Japan of battleships of 46,000 tons led the United States, Britain and France to invoke the "Escalator Clause" of the London Treaty of 1936, was it possible for the US Navy to contemplate true fast battleships. On a maximum displacement of 45,000 tons it proved possible to make some improvements in firepower (by adopting a 50cal. main gun in place of the 45cal. model installed in the earlier two classes) and in protection, and at the same time to increase installed horsepower from 130,000shp to 200,000shp, for a designed speed of 33kt. This speed was attained with ease during sea trials, making the ships the fastest battleships of World War II. ▶

Below: *New Jersey* in company with the carrier *Hancock,* December 1944. As with the two previous classes, the Iowas operated with the carrier task forces, but for the first time a maximum speed similar to that of the fleet carriers was provided.

Above: *Iowa* in the Pacific at the end of World War II. The long, narrow bow section was necessitated by the requirement for high speed, but the ships were very wet forward.

Above: *Missouri* fires her big guns during the final months of World War II. She and *Wisconsin* entered service only in late 1944, but *Missouri* was chosen as the venue for the signing of the Japanese terms of surrender on 2 September 1945.

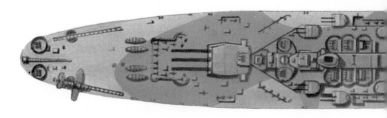

Above: A plan view of *Missouri* in July 1944. Note the layout of the 40mm mountings, which have been positioned well away from the big guns.

The rationale for high speed, which was extremely costly in terms of displacement and additional protection, was the fear that the Japanese would form fast carrier task forces comprising carriers and large heavy cruisers to harass US lines of communication in the early stages of a Pacific War. There was also a possibility that the battlecruisers of the Kongo class would be detached from the battle force in support of these groups — an assessment which events were to prove absolutely correct. The initial order was for four ships, and two further units, *Illinois* (BB65), and *Kentucky* (BB66), were added in 1940 as part of an emergency construction programme.

The protection system was similar in principle to that of the *South Dakota*, but with important modifications. The belt, which was again tapered below the waterline and which extended to the ship's bottom, was no longer sloped internally, but was attached directly to the hull plating; drag at high speeds was reduced by fitting the armour plate to the inside rather than the outside of the plating. Four longitudinal torpedo bulkheads were placed inside the tapered belt, thereby avoiding some of the problems experienced with the underwater protection system of the South Dakotas. A remarkable feature of the class was the provision of two heavily armoured decks, with a splinter deck between them. The armoured decks had a combined thickness of about 12in (305mm), giving the ships unequalled protection against plunging shells and bombs.

The additional length necessitated by the increase in horsepower was utilised to provide a well-spaced secondary armament of 5in (127mm)/38cal. DP guns and large numbers of quadruple 40mm mountings. Because the arrangements were much less cramped than in their predecessors there was far less mutual interference between the various AA mountings in terms of training arcs and blast damage. *Iowa*, like *South Dakota*, was designed as a force flagship with an enlarged conning tower which precluded the installation of a 40mm mounting atop "B" turret. She was therefore completed with 60 x 40mm (later increased to 76), four less than her sister *New Jersey*, while the two later units were fitted with 80 x 40mm from the outset. *Iowa* also carried 60 x 20mm AA, but some of these were later replaced by 40mm mountings, and

Right: An aerial view of *New Jersey* after she had been reactivated to serve as a command and fire support ship during the Vietnam War, to which theatre she was deployed in 1968-69.

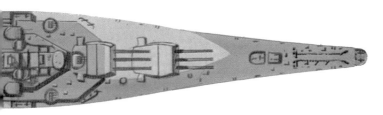

Below: The elegant, well-balanced profile of the
Iowa was in marked contrast to the compact,
somewhat cramped arrangements in the South
Dakota class. This is *Missouri,* July 1944.

by 1945 the four ships of the class mounted 49–57 x 20mm in single and twin
mountings. Although *Iowa* was the only ship of the class with specially designed flag accommodation, the other units proved equally well-suited to the flag
function because of their size advantage over earlier types. There were two
catapults, and three aircraft could be accommodated.

Iowa entered service in the Atlantic in August 1943, and for the next two
months was employed on escort duties off Newfoundland in anticipation of a
breakout by the battleship *Tirpitz.* From January 1944 she and her recently
completed sister *New Jersey* were in the Pacific, where they accompanied the
fast carrier task forces in the campaign against the Japanese-held island
chains. Both were present at the Battle of the Philippine Sea and at Leyte Gulf.
Missouri and *Wisconsin* were not in service until late 1944, but were present
for the assaults on Iwo Jima and Okinawa, and accompanied the fast carrier
task forces in the final raids on Japan. *Missouri* sustained slight damage when ▶

struck by a kamikaze off Okinawa, but later had the distinction of being the ship on which the Japanese surrender was signed in Tokyo Bay.

The fifth and sixth units of the class were never completed. *Illinois* was cancelled in August 1945, by which time she was only 22 per cent complete. The construction of *Kentucky* was halted in 1947, but was resumed in 1948. Work was then halted while plans for conversion to a missile configuration (BBG) were considered, but these were finally abandoned in 1958, and the hull was scrapped the following year. The turbines were used to power the first two vessels of a new class of Fast Combat Support Ships, *Sacramento* (AOE1) and *Camden* (AOE2).

The Iowas were soon to be reactivated to provide task force flagships and fire support for US ground forces in the Korean War. Each ship undertook a six-month deployment before being relieved by another vessel of the class, the sequence being as follows: *Missouri* September 1950 to March 1951; *New Jersey* May 1951 to November 1951; *Wisconsin* November 1951 to March 1952; *Iowa* April 1952 to October 1952; and *Missouri* again from October 1952 to March 1953. During this period *New Jersey*, *Missouri* and *Wisconsin* were fitted with an SPS-8A 3-D radar for aircraft direction atop a modified lattice mainmast. In 1956 *Wisconsin* was in collision with the destroyer *Eaton*, and had 70ft (20m) of her bow replaced using the bow from the uncompleted *Kentucky*. All four ships were again in reserve by 1958.

New Jersey was again recommissioned in 1968 because of a shortage of big-gun cruisers to provide fire support for US ground forces in the Vietnam War. Her recommissioning was not without opposition, and she received only an austere modernisation. All light AA weapons had been removed by this time, and in the absence of a credible aerial threat *New Jersey* carried in their place only 5in (127mm) Zuni chaff rocket launchers to decoy "Styx" missiles launched from North Korean FPBs. The fire control and surveillance radars remained unchanged, but the ESM and communications outfit was upgraded. During ▶

Right: *New Jersey* fires a full salvo during fire support operations. During her brief commissioning for Vietnam, she fired no fewer than 5,688 16in shells at enemy positions ashore.

Below: *New Jersey* received only a token refurbishment (principally updated communications and new ECM) for her duties off Vietnam.

her brief commission *New Jersey* fired no fewer than 5,688 16in shells at shore targets (in the last two years of World War II she had fired only 771!). However, her critics remained active, and she was decommissioned at the end of 1969 as she was preparing for a second deployment.

In 1973 the US Navy seriously considered disposing of the *Iowas,* but they were retained in reserve because of a continuing shortage of fire support vessels, and also because of their lack of active service. In 1975 the first proposals for missile-armed Surface Action Groups (SAGs) centred on the battleships were put forward. It was envisaged that SAGs would operate in low-threat areas which did not justify the presence of a carrier battle group, thereby compensating for the diminishing number of carriers available. The movement to make funds available to refurbish the *Iowas* gathered strength in the late 1970s, and after some controversy the modernisation of *New Jersey* was finally authorised as part of the Reagan Supplemental Budget FY81. The total cost was $326 million, of which $170 million was for rehabilitation and the remainder for new weapons systems and electronics. Four of the 5in (127mm) twin turrets were removed to make space for a formidable array of surface-to-

Above: *New Jersey* fires a surface-to-surface missile during the early 1980s. As modified she carries 32 Tomahawk long-range cruise missiles in armoured box launchers, and 16 Harpoon medium-range SSMs. Four twin 5in/38cal. mountings have been removed in compensation.

Right: A close-up of one of *New Jersey*'s Phalanx Close-In Weapon Systems (CIWS). Phalanx comprises a 20mm gun mounting with six rotating barrels and a quick-reaction on-mount radar. As modified *New Jersey* has four Phalanx mountings, backed up by eight Super RBOC Mk 36 chaff launchers.

Above: *New Jersey* as she appeared in **1983** following reactivation. The lower drawing shows how she might have appeared after the proposed Phase II reconstruction, in which a hangar and flight deck for V/STOL aircraft would have replaced the third 16in gun turret. This proposal was rejected as too costly.

surface missiles. There are now eight quadruple armoured box launchers for Tomahawk anti-ship and land-attack missiles forward and aft of the second funnel, and four quadruple launchers for Harpoon anti-ship missiles abreast the funnel. Anti-missile defences have been boosted by the provision of four Phalanx CIWS, Super RBOC chaff launchers and the SLQ-32 ECM system. The mainmast has been removed altogether, and there is now an SPS-49 air surveillance radar atop the foremast tower. The stern has been cleared for one operating helicopter spot and three parking spots, and the ship's boilers have been converted to burn Navy distillate fuel instead of black oil. Following her recommissioning in 1983 *New Jersey* was deployed to the US Sixth Fleet in the Mediterranean, where she provided fire support for US Marines in the Lebanon.

The refurbishment of *Iowa* was funded under FY82 and FY83, and she recommissioned in the spring of 1984. The third ship, *Missouri*, will be funded under FY85, but there is some doubt as to whether *Wisconsin* will be refitted, given a tightening budget.

Below: *New Jersey* following her reactivation in 1982. Note the heavy lattice foremast with its SPS-49 air surveillance radar.

Alaska Class

Names: *Alaska* (CB1), *Guam* (CB2), *Hawaii* (CB3).
Laid down: 1941–43.
Completed: 1944.
Displacement: 29,780 tons standard; 34,250 tons full load.
Dimensions: Length 808ft 6in (246·4m) oa; beam 91ft 1in (27·8m); draught 31ft 10in (9·7m).
Propulsion: General Electric geared steam turbines, 8 Babcock & Wilcox boilers; 150,000shp; 4 shafts; 33kt.
Armour: Belt 9in–5in (230–125mm); decks 1·4in + 3·8in (35mm + 95mm); barbettes 13in–11in (330–280mm); turrets 12·8in–5in (325–125mm); conning tower 10·6in–5in (270–125mm).
Armament: 9 x 12in (305mm); 12 x 5in (127mm) DP; 56 x 40mm AA; 30–34 x 20mm AA.
Complement: 1,517.

Above: *Alaska* shortly after her completion in July 1944. Although officially designated "large cruisers" (CB), these ships were similar in many respects to the largely discredited battlecruiser type, with big guns but relatively light armour.

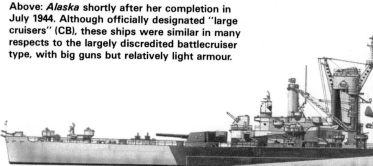

Development: Although generally considered to be capital ships, the Alaska class were rated as "large cruisers" by the US Navy. The origins of the type are somewhat confused, falling somewhere between a requirement for a "super-cruiser" with the speed and firepower to catch and destroy 8in (203mm) gun cruisers, and a perceived requirement to counter a new class of battlecruisers rumoured to be under construction for Japan in 1940–41. The ability to operate with the carrier task forces was a primary requirement, as it was consided that the Japanese would deploy their powerful force of 8in (203mm) cruisers and the new battlecruisers in similar fashion. Propulsion machinery similar to that of the Essex class carriers was therefore installed, for a speed of 33kt.

The 12in (305mm) gun was developed specifically for this class. The initial design allowed for only eight guns in one twin and two triple mountings, but this was revised to three triples in order to simplify turret production. The 5in (127mm)/38cal. secondary battery was on a par with the 8in (203mm) cruisers of the contemporary Baltimore class, but the great length of the Alaskas allowed additional 40mm mountings to be worked in. Other cruiser features included a single rudder — which unfortunately resulted in a large turning ▶

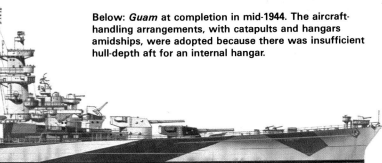

Below: *Guam* at completion in mid-1944. The aircraft-handling arrangements, with catapults and hangars amidships, were adopted because there was insufficient hull-depth aft for an internal hangar.

circle — and two trainable catapults (four aircraft) amidships. The last US ships to have this arrangement were the heavy cruisers of the New Orleans class; it was revived in the Alaskas because there was insufficient hull depth aft for a between-decks hangar.

The ambiguity of the ships' design requirements can be seen in the relatively light armour protection. Initially it was intended to fit armour sufficient to resist 12in (305mm) shellfire over the main magazines, with protection only against 8in (203mm) shells over the machinery. In the event the thickness of armour above the machinery had to be increased because of the location of the midships 5in (127mm) magazines, but although protection against 12in (305mm) shellfire would have proved more than adequate had the ships encountered Japanese heavy cruisers, it would not have enabled them to take on any of the Japanese battleships — even the elderly Kongos — with any degree of confidence. As for the Japanese battlecruisers, these were cancelled after the success of the carriers at Pearl Harbor, before any orders had been placed. Nevertheless, the Alaskas proved to be excellent carrier escorts because of their high speed, good endurance, and powerful anti-aircraft batteries; they were highly regarded in the US fleet, even though their operational careers proved to be rather brief.

Alaska first deployed in January 1945, being present at the assaults on Iwo Jima and Okinawa. She was joined in March by her sister *Guam* and both ships participated in the final carrier raids on Japan. They were subsequently placed in reserve in 1947, and were sold for scrap in 1961.

The third ship, *Hawaii,* was 82·4 per cent complete in August 1945, when work was halted. She was transferred to Philadelphia for conversion to a missile ship in 1946, but this plan was abandoned the following year. It was subsequently proposed to convert her into a tactical command ship to serve with the carrier task forces, but the cost of conversion proved prohibitive and the hull was sold for scrap in 1959. Three further units of the class were projected, but when it became known that the Japanese had not proceeded with the construction of their own battlecruisers, these were cancelled in June 1943; the names *Philippines, Puerto Rico* and *Samoa* had been allocated.

Below: *Alaska* **in 1944. Fast, moderately well protected, and carrying an array of light AA weapons on a par with contemporary US battleships,** *Alaska* **and** *Guam* **proved to be excellent carrier escorts. They were, however, withdrawn from service shortly after the end of World War II and were never reactivated.**

OTHER SUPER-VALUE MILITARY GUIDES IN THIS SERIES......

AN ILLUSTRATED GUIDE TO

MODERN SUBMARINES

The undersea weapons that rule the oceans today

160 fact-packed pages
Over 130 photographs,
many in colour
More than 60
detailed
line drawings

An international survey
of more than
70 submarine classes
Full details of
boats, weapons
and tactics

David Miller

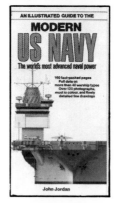

AN ILLUSTRATED GUIDE TO THE

MODERN US NAVY

The world's most advanced naval power

160 fact-packed pages
Full data on
more than 40 warship types
Over 120 photographs,
most in colour, and finely
detailed line drawings

John Jordan

AN ILLUSTRATED GUIDE TO

MODERN SUB HUNTERS

Major weapons used
to track and
destroy enemy
submarines today

Over 40 systems:
ships and aircraft,
sensors and missiles,
all illustrated

Lt. Col. David Miller

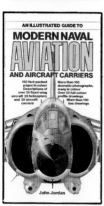

AN ILLUSTRATED GUIDE TO

MODERN NAVAL AVIATION

AND AIRCRAFT CARRIERS

160 fact-packed
pages in colour
Descriptions of
over 30 fixed-wing
aircraft, 20 helicopters
and 20 aircraft
carriers

More than 100
dramatic photographs,
many in colour
Over 30 full-colour
profile drawings
More than 100
line drawings

John Jordan

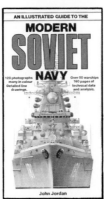

AN ILLUSTRATED GUIDE TO THE

MODERN SOVIET NAVY

120 photographs
many in colour
Detailed line
drawings

Over 50 warships
160 pages of
technical data
and analysis.

John Jordan

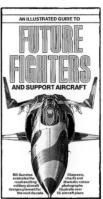

AN ILLUSTRATED GUIDE TO

FUTURE FIGHTERS

AND SUPPORT AIRCRAFT

Bill Gunston
evaluates the
most exciting
military aircraft
designs planned for
the next decade

Diagrams,
charts and
dramatic colour
photographs
illustrate over
35 aircraft plans

OTHER ILLUSTRATED MILITARY GUIDES NOW AVAILABLE.

Air War over Vietnam
Allied Fighters of World War II
Bombers of World War II
German, Italian and Japanese
  Fighters of World War II
Israeli Air Force
Military Helicopters
Modern Elite Forces
Modern Fighters and Attack Aircraft
Modern Soviet Air Force

Modern Soviet Ground Forces
Modern Tanks
Modern US Air Force
Modern US Army
Modern Warships
Pistols and Revolvers
Rifles and Sub-Machine Guns
Spyplanes and Electronic
  Warfare Aircraft
World War II Tanks

✳ Each has 160 fact-filled pages
✳ Each is colourfully illustrated with hundreds of action photographs and technical drawings
✳ Each contains concisely presented data and accurate descriptions of major
  international weapons
✳ Each represents tremendous value